THE *PREVALENCE* OF *PEOPLE*

BOOKS BY MARSTON BATES

THE PREVALENCE OF PEOPLE

WHERE WINTER NEVER COMES

THE NATURE OF NATURAL HISTORY

THE NATURAL HISTORY OF MOSQUITOES

MARSTON BATES   DELLENBACK

MARSTON BATES began to study the problem of mosquito biology for the Rockefeller Foundation in 1935 in Albania, on leave of absence from the Museum of Comparative Zoology at Harvard. He resigned from Harvard in 1937 to join the staff of the International Health Division of the Foundation. Four years in Albania, a year in Egypt, and eight years in Colombia were devoted to yellow fever and malaria research. Following his inquiry into the human population problem, he entered academic life. In his professorship of Zoology at the University of Michigan he is interested primarily in finding out how the various biological and social sciences, as cultivated in a university, fit together to give a better understanding of the human "animal."

THE PREVALENCE OF PEOPLE

by MARSTON BATES

CHARLES SCRIBNER'S SONS

NEW YORK, *1955*

COPYRIGHT SOURCES QUOTED

Hailey, Lord [Malcolm], *AN AFRICAN SURVEY,* Oxford University Press, New York, 1938.

Himes, Norman, *MEDICAL HISTORY OF CONTRACEPTION,* Williams & Wilkins Co., Baltimore, 1936.

Keys, Ancel, J. Brozek, A. Henschel, O. Mickelsen and H. L. Taylor, *THE BIOLOGY OF HUMAN STARVATION,* University of Minnesota Press, Minneapolis, 1950.

Kroeber, A. L., *CULTURAL AND NATURAL AREAS OF NATIVE NORTH AMERICA,* University of California Press, Berkeley, 1939.

Kuczynski, R. R., *DEMOGRAPHIC SURVEY OF THE BRITISH COLONIAL EMPIRE,* Vol. I, Oxford University Press, New York, 1948.

Lorenz, K. Z., *KING SOLOMON'S RING,* Thomas Y. Crowell Co., New York, 1952.

Osborn, Frederick, *PREFACE TO EUGENICS,* Harper & Bros., New York, 1940.

Richards, Audry I., *HUNGER AND WORK IN A SAVAGE TRIBE,* George Routledge & Sons, London, 1932.

Salaman, R. N., *THE HISTORY AND SOCIAL INFLUENCE OF THE POTATO,* University Press, Cambridge, 1949.

Sigerist, H. E., *MEDICINE AND HUMAN WELFARE,* Yale University Press, New Haven, 1941.

Solecki, Ralph, *HOW MAN CAME TO NORTH AMERICA,* Scientific American, New York, 1951.

Spencer, Sir Baldwin and F. J. Gillen, *THE ARUNTA,* Macmillan & Co., London, 1927.

Stearn, E. W. and A. E. Stearn, *THE EFFECT OF SMALLPOX ON THE DESTINY OF THE AMERINDIAN,* Humphries, Inc., Boston, 1945.

Stern, B. J., *SOCIETY AND MEDICAL PROGRESS,* Princeton University Press, Princeton, 1941.

Strachey, G. L., *PORTRAITS IN MINIATURE AND OTHER ESSAYS,* Chatto & Windus, London, 1931.

Thompson, Warren, *POPULATION PROBLEMS,* McGraw-Hill Book Co., New York, 1953.

Winslow, C. E. A., *MAN AND EPIDEMICS,* Princeton University Press, Princeton, 1952.

Wright, Quincy, *A STUDY OF WAR,* University of Chicago Press, Chicago, 1942.

Zinsser, Hans, *BATS, LICE AND HISTORY,* Little, Brown & Co., Boston, 1935.

THE PREPARATION OF THIS BOOK was greatly facilitated by a grant from the Division of Social Sciences of the Rockefeller Foundation. The material was used, in the summer of 1954, for the Timothy Hopkins Lectures at the Hopkins Marine Station of Stanford University.

M. B.

Contents

THE PREVALENCE OF PEOPLE

CHAPTER *1* FROM MOSQUITOES TO PEOPLE

The beginning of this book can be dated quite precisely as Tuesday, October 26th, 1948. The timing can be narrowed down to about four o'clock in the afternoon, to an interview with Dr. George K. Strode, then director of the International Health Division of the Rockefeller Foundation. He was my chief and the topic for discussion was my next assignment.

After some polite preliminaries, Dr. Strode turned to me rather abruptly and asked, "How would you like to study the human population problem, from your point of view as a biologist?"

This was a complete surprise.

"What do you mean?"

He went on to explain. We were living in a time when some people were beginning to question the philosophy and value of public health work as now carried out. He and other public health men were increasingly subject to jibes about public

1

health being a "bad thing"—sometimes jokingly, sometimes half-seriously, sometimes in deadly earnest. Public health, by forestalling death through disease, might be creating a new problem as it solved an old one, might simply be providing more tinder for death by starvation in the overcrowded countries of the world, might be changing the disease problem into a population problem.

Was there any truth in what the alarmists said? And, in any case, could we deal with public health as a separate sort of enterprise, a thing-in-itself, apart from the economic and social problems of the peoples concerned? Public health, as an instrument for the control of disease, was clearly an instrument of social change. It would seem that we should at least try to use this instrument with an awareness of the total biological and social situation in which we are working. But how could we achieve such awareness?

Dr. Strode had no answer. He knew I had no answer. But he thought that a public health organization ought to be trying to find answers to such questions, and he knew I might be interested in taking part in the search.

It seemed, on the surface, a bizarre proposal to make to a biologist who came straight from eight years of residence in a remote part of the interior of South America, and whose previous concern had been chiefly with mosquitoes and viruses. But I jumped at the chance to move into a new area of thought, as Dr. Strode knew I would.

During those years in South America I had become increasingly interested in general problems—in the nature of science, and the role of science and scientists in our civilization. I suspect this was partly a symptom of the onset of middle age, partly a reaction to the puzzling times in which we live. There was, in that remote South American town, plenty of time for thinking; I wrote some sententious articles which, fortunately, were never published, and I started working on a book which has subsequently appeared under the title of *The Nature of Natural History*. Thus I gradually worked myself into an awareness of the social responsibility of science, of the importance of at least trying to see, as an individual, how the point of view and the information of biology might be relevant to the preoccupations and problems of our own species. So my shift from mosquitoes to people, from Villavicencio to New York, was perhaps not as abrupt and illogical as it might seem at first sight.

I started on my new assignment by visiting several universities and talking with a variety of people who had been working on one aspect or another of the problems of man's population growth. One of the first men on my list was Lowell Reed, that wise mathematician who is now president of the Johns Hopkins University. He countered my questioning with another question—

"What do you mean by 'population problem'?" And he continued with the advice, "Start out by trying to define your terms."

So I went off to brood about this for a while. It is easy to talk about the population problem, even to shout about it; but it turns out to be much more difficult to say what it is you are talking about—or shouting about. I went around in circles, dropping memoranda at each turn, for a whole summer; the end result, as might be expected, was not clarity, but a state of dizzy confusion. The population problem seemed to have become transformed into a sort of general mist which we call "human ecology." I have begun to suspect that you can make almost anything disappear if you try hard enough to define it.

The best I could do was to say that the population problem, in the first place, was the problem of finding out the densities of population most favorable for human activities and purposes in relation to available resources; and, in the second place, the problem of achieving and maintaining such densities, if they could be determined.

This sounds all right if you read it fast enough. But if you stop to look at it closely, you will find that the words disappear into this general mist that I spoke of as human ecology—the interrelations of man and the environment in which he lives. The mist might better be called "the phenomenon of the inter-relatedness of things." My attempt at definition, instead of narrowing the problem, had widened it out until it seemed to coincide with the possible universe of human knowledge.

Population densities, where we start, seem simple enough— a matter of number of people per square mile or per acre or some other unit of area. Changes in density, with man or any other animal, will result from changes in the relation between numbers of births and numbers of deaths, with migration to be taken into account if we are dealing with a limited area.

Births, deaths, migrations—these are all things that the scientist can deal with statistically. He can analyze and describe the biological and social factors that seem to govern birth rates and death rates; he can point out trends, make predictions, draw neat graphs, and create a nice feeling of precision. But what do these figures mean? They have to be looked at in terms of both resources and purposes—which gets us into difficulties.

"Resources" seems a concrete enough word when you first look at it. It refers to things like soil fertility, oil reserves, water power. These, too, can be calculated. There are certain obvious difficulties—different people, for instance, may arrive at quite different figures for the oil reserves of the world. But the real difficulty turns on the fact that the meaning of resources is relative rather than absolute. We can see this easily enough if we look into the past: the resources of the area covered by the United States had one meaning for the pre-Columbian Indians; they have a quite different meaning for our contemporary industrial economy. We have seen the meaning of uranium as a resource change in the past few years. If there have been such great changes in the past, how can we look toward the future? The Sahara desert would have no place in a current list of the major resources behind human economy, but what if we come to depend primarily on solar energy for power?

"Purposes" is an even trickier word, but I don't see how we can escape it. The densities and the resources and the ways of using the resources all become relative to purpose: whether the goal is power for a particular segment of mankind; whether the goal is material, in the sense of production of wealth; whether the goal is "happiness"—the greatest good for the greatest number. But what is "good"? When we start speculating about these things, we have long since left the area of knowledge ordinarily called science and got into philosophy, ethics, religion, the arts, the humanities that deal with the hopes, fears, aspirations, pleasures and the intangible burdens of mankind.

Biological science has blended with social science, both have become involved with the technologies based on the physical sciences, and the whole thing seems to have meaning only in terms of ideas of value that we think of as belonging primarily to the humanities. My attempt at definition had got me thoroughly entangled with the interrelatedness of things.

This was not of much help from the immediate point of view of planning public health operations, except to underline what we all knew already, that public health was an integral part of the whole social fabric and needed to be dealt with as such. It was clear enough, without these mental acrobatics of mine, that it would be valuable to have sociologists and anthropologists working with physicians and nurses on public health teams, and many organizations have started experiments of this sort.

But the impractical, theoretical implications of these relationships interested me most. The Rockefeller Foundation is a tolerant organization. My chiefs let me put aside the immediate public health question that had started me off, while I wandered fuzzily around trying to learn something about the various kinds of studies that touched on this broad population question.

I found many other people puzzling over the interrelatedness of things. In the universities there were seminars, conferences, study groups, made up of experts in different fields trying to learn one another's technical language, trying to relate one another's ideas and concepts. All sorts of questions were being tackled by research teams, and "interdisciplinary studies" were the latest thing on every campus.

For a while this worried me. It looked as though I were following a fashion in wandering from biology into the sciences of man. No scientist likes to think he is following a current fashion; he likes to feel he is original, or ahead of his time, striking out boldly into the unknown. I finally comforted myself by a trick of rephrasing. I decided, not that I was following a fashion, but that I was working in a favorable climate of opinion. That seemed perfectly respectable.

In 1952 I moved to the University of Michigan where I could live right in the middle of all of these disciplines and take an active part in the academic search for interrelations. Most of this book has been written in Ann Arbor, and it constitutes a sort of progress report on my search for understanding.

I have started on this personal note partly as an explanation of how I happened to get involved with population questions, and partly as a warning to the reader. I can lay no claim to being expert on any of the topics discussed in the book. I have tried to mirror expert opinion as faithfully as I could, but my mirror may well be cracked or full of wavy distortions caused by my ignorance or my prejudices.

My particular object has been to try to blend the materials and the viewpoints of a variety of sciences insofar as they are involved in this particular topic of the present and past population behavior of man. I have tried, particularly, to put together pertinent parts of biology, sociology, anthropology and history.

It sounds very serious when I write it out like this, but I have tried to deal with these materials lightly. It seems to me that serious subjects often need to be treated lightly—that therein lies our escape from madness, that therein lies our hope of reconciling the apparently irreconcilable.

The biological point of view probably still predominates in this book—but always tempered, I hope, by an awareness of the peculiar circumstances of man, whose behavior is so largely moulded by nonbiological factors. I have tried to analyze the interplay of biological and cultural factors in a chapter grandly titled "The Nature of Men," which follows directly after a rapid survey of what we know about the numbers of men in present and past times. That glance at the puzzle of human nature is followed by a chapter on human varieties—and here again we have to consider both biological and cultural classifications.

After looking at the numbers, nature and kinds of men, it seems logical to consider how they live, their varied means of subsistence or economies. The proposition of Malthus, that population tends to live up to food supply, needs to be examined here; and since this has been taken as a sort of general law of nature, we shall have to look at the ecology of animals as well as the economics of man.

The size and growth of a population depends on the additions (reproduction) and the losses (mortality), with the additional factor of migration in and out if the population is defined in terms of some geographical area. These topics make up the body of the book. I have tried, generally, to deal with them in the context of history; that is, not only to look at the present situation of man, but also to consider the historical or evolutionary processes that may have brought this situation about.

In the last part of the book I have included a chapter on eugenics, on various theories about how we might improve the breed of man, since this has been a preoccupation of many biologists. And then, in brief compass, I have tried to survey the various sciences that have been concerned with these questions of human populations—a part of man's effort to understand himself by using the tools of science. Finally, I have tried to look at the meaning of all of this, in a sort of feeble essay into the role of science in human affairs.

Our proper start, then, is with a statement of the population situation—an estimate of the numbers of men now living on the earth, some analysis of their distribution over the various geographical regions, and some account of what we know of population history in these various regions.

CHAPTER **2** THE NUMBERS OF MEN

No one knows exactly how many people there are in the world today because the teeming inhabitants of Asia and Africa have never been counted, and because the counts, in most places where they have been made, are subject to errors of one sort or another. The most careful and reasonable estimates place the total for the globe somewhere between two billion and two billion and a half—figures beyond the grasp of any ordinary imagination. Man, clearly, is a very abundant animal; perhaps the most abundant of all of the mammals.

Rats and mice, to be sure, are also common. The total number of living rodents is much larger than the total number of living men. Someone has estimated that in a few very favorable places there may be as many as 12,000 field mice in a single acre of land (I calculate that there are about 137 people per acre on Manhattan). With such figures, Ivan Sanderson has guessed that there may be somewhere between ten billion and ten trillion rodents of all sorts on the continent of North America.

But there are over 300 different species of rodents involved

9

in such an estimate—field mice and town mice, gray rats and brown rats, squirrels and chipmunks, kept distinct by barriers of sexual sterility. Living man, on the other hand, is but a single species, since the brown and yellow and whitish varieties show themselves perfectly capable of interbreeding wherever they come in contact. To be fair, we should compare man with some single species of rodent, such as the brown rat.

Dr. David Davis of the Johns Hopkins University has been making careful studies of the rat population in the city of Baltimore for several years. He estimated a rat population of 400,000 for the city in 1944, which declined to 165,000 by 1947, and to 65,000 by 1949. The human population of Baltimore, meanwhile, varied from 859,000 in 1940 to 950,00 in 1950. Conditions in Baltimore may be unusually favorable for people and unfavorable for rats, and we would have to have statistics for a variety of places before drawing any sweeping conclusions. But if Baltimore can be taken as any indication, man is keeping well ahead of the rats.

To find animals that are clearly more abundant than man, you have to turn to things like codfish, sardines, grasshoppers, and houseflies. Bacteria, of course, really put us to shame. But a bacterium can reproduce itself in a half hour or so; while man takes nine months of gestation and then long years of growing up, so that the average generation covers a span of nearly thirty years. Man's achievement, with this handicap, is really remarkable.

The extreme abundance of the human species is a recent phenomenon. During the present century, the human population of the earth has been increasing at a regular rate of about one per cent per year. One student, Dr. C. B. Fawcett, has calculated that "if this had been the average rate of increase in the past, the whole of the present population of the world would be descended from a couple living near the end of the first century B.C. If it could be maintained in the future, then in another thousand years the earth would have about 25 millions of millions of human inhabitants, which would be more than one to every square yard of land."

No one has suggested that man got started in 100 B.C. The careful scriptural calculations of Bishop Ussher would have Adam and Eve created in 4004 B.C. (on October 31st); and contemporary scientific opinion gives man not 2,000 years, nor 6,000 years, but about half a million years in which to reach his present prevalence. As for the future, even the most optimistic prophets of ever-expanding resources and ever-growing human communities have not calculated on maintaining those 25 millions of millions a thousand years hence—a human for every square yard of land. Manhattan seems rather crowded now with something like 35 square yards per inhabitant. The rate of growth will surely change even before the Sahara has become as crowded as Manhattan Island is today.

But if the 25 millions of millions are unthinkable, what will be the limit, and how will it be attained? Will we breed right up to some margin of bare subsistence, where the balance of population will teeter indefinitely in misery and periodic starvation? Or will we solve the matter by recurrent warfare, killing off whole masses of excess people with the occasional explosion of a few superbombs? Or will our breeding habits change—and is such change an inevitable result of forces at work in our economy, or must it be brought about by deliberate action, by legislation, birth control propaganda, education and the like? And is "stability" our goal? It seems a horrid word to us, brought up, as we have been, in an ever-expanding economy and nourished on the idea of progress.

The questions, as I have phrased them, look to the future, which means that the answers can never be certain until that future has changed into present. But we can frame similar questions about the present and the past, and for these we can hope to find answers. Knowing the present and the past, we can at least be better prepared for the future. Which gives a special "importance" to studies of population.

Even if the problems of the prevalence of people were not important, they would still be interesting. Man is an endlessly fascinating subject of study for man, and the pull for introspection is always with us. We cannot help wondering why we are such fools, occasionally wondering how we find such pleasant satisfactions, being bewildered by our complexities, driven by our simplicities—and striving for that understanding that always seems to be just beyond our reach. This wonder, this curiosity, surely is excuse enough for looking at our numbers.

The figure most commonly used for the human population of the world, as of midyear 1950, is 2,400 million. This is based on census results and estimates from the various countries of the world collected and evaluated by the Statistical Office and the Population Division of the United Nations.

The United Nations, of course, can only collect the reports and estimates of the various governments—it can't initiate and carry out actual census operations. Since the accuracy of the statistics for different parts of the world varies greatly, a large element of uncertainty enters into the totals. The actual U.N. estimate for 1950 was that the world population was somewhere between 2,350 and 2,471 million, with 2,411 million as an average of the estimates. If we round out the figures, and break this down by continents, we get the following results:

Europe	559,000,000
Anglo-America	166,000,000
Latin America	162,000,000
Oceania & Australia	13,000,000
Africa	198,000,000
Asia	1,302,000,000
TOTAL	2,400,000,000

The figure for Europe would be fairly definite, if it weren't for the Soviet Union, which seems to be reluctant about exporting statistics. The figure generally used for the USSR as a whole is 193 million, which derives from a 1946 estimate. The Soviets seem to disapprove of the idea of a European continent, because the statistics that are available do not break up readily into European and Asiatic parts. The Russian Socialist Federated Soviet Republic, one of the constituents of the Union, extends from the Baltic to the Pacific, with the Ural mountains a mere geographical incident part way across. This may be a rebellion against the old days, when Russia in Europe and Russia in Asia got separate statistical treatment; but it makes comparisons between the old statistics and the new difficult. I have rather arbitrarily allotted 30 million of the Russians to Siberia, leaving 163 million for Europe, to get my figure for the continent.

Canada and the United States, which I have lumped as Anglo-America, have definite census figures which are considered to be quite accurate. The figure for Latin America is much more uncertain, and it may be off by several million. The Oceania and Australia figure is mostly Australia (about 8 million) and New Zealand (about 2 million).

The estimate of 198 million people for Africa can really hardly be called more than an informed guess, though the *Demographic Yearbook* considers that the total is probably somewhere between 189 million and 205 million. This is a small possible error compared with that for Asia, where the errors in estimates may add up to a hundred million persons or so.

The big uncertainty is China. Probably no one, not even the present government of China, has a very exact idea of how many people inhabit the country. The most ingenious methods have been used for arriving at estimates; yet these may differ from one another by as much as fifty million people. Each estimate seems equally plausible (or implausible) to an outsider. The latest official figures (for 1948) give a population of 463,-493,000 people—or about a fifth of the total for the world. The figures for India have a solider basis than those for China, though there are still elements of uncertainty. The 1951 census of the Republic of India gave a population of 356,829,485, which sounds precise enough. Pakistan has about 75 million inhabitants. The two countries of the subcontinent of India, then, include almost another fifth of the total population of the world; and Asia as a whole, no matter how you make the calculations, comes out with more than half of the world's total of people.

My wife, reading through an early draft of this chapter, complained that she got dizzy with the statistics. Rather regretfully, then, I have cut out most of the figures in rewriting. I could arrange them in tables, I suppose, but I know myself that I tend to skip tables of figures when I am reading a book, so there is not much point in tables, either. Maybe detailed statistics are not needed: I only want to give a general idea of the numbers of men, their distribution over the earth, and the uncertainty that should go with many of the figures. The details, to be sure, can be found in any number of reference books and there is no use in repeating them here. The reference books often fail to emphasize the uncertainty, since they give equally precise figures for countries in western Europe and for colonies in Africa, though the first are based on quite accurate counts and the second on estimates that might better be called guesses.

The uncertainty of our population figures for much of the world needs to be emphasized, I think. The difficulties of making censuses in the non-Western parts of the world are immense. I like the phrasing of a student of African population who wrote that "to appraise fertility, morbidity, mortality, or migrations is about as difficult in most African dependencies as to appraise the frequency of adultery in England." You could probably get figures for adultery in England—Mr. Kinsey has them for the United States—but the difficulties and the uncertainties are clear enough.

Yet the population figures for the world have been worked over by many different people, checked in many different ways, until there can be no doubt about their general reliability, however uncertain some of the details may be.

The earth has a little over 57 million square miles of land surface. If the people were scattered uniformly over this land, then, there would be about 42 inhabitants for every square mile. But the distribution is clearly far from uniform. The six million square miles of Antarctica have no inhabitants at all; and the ice sheets, tundras, and deserts of other continents add about 14 million more square miles to the area completely uninhabited by man. At the other extreme, the island of Java has over 1,000 inhabitants per square mile, Belgium has 740 inhabitants per square mile, Puerto Rico about 600. Large areas of the Orient—Japan, Korea, eastern China, the East Indies generally—average between 400 and 500 inhabitants per square mile. The average density of population in Western and Central Europe is about 310 per square mile; in the continental United States as a whole, 50.7 per square mile. In the northeastern United States, where the population reaches its greatest density, there is an average of about 180 inhabitants per square mile—still a thin population compared with the Orient or Europe.

It turns out that two-thirds of the world's inhabitants live crowded into about four and a quarter million square miles of land—less than 8 per cent of the total land surface. These densely populated areas are the Far East, the Indian subcontinent, western and central Europe, and the northeastern United States.

These statistics on the prevalence of people in the world today can be analyzed in many sorts of ways. By racial groupings, the "whites" are in a majority—about 57 per cent of the total. More than half of these "whites" are Europeans or direct descendants of European stock on other continents; the rest are the Hindus, Iranians and Arabs of Asia and North Africa. Of the total, 34 per cent belong to the "Mongoloid" races; which leaves 9 per cent for the various "Negro" races.

If we divide the world total by religion, we find that about 32 per cent is Christian, of one sort or another, 27 per cent Buddhist, 17 per cent Hindu, and 13 per cent Mohammedan. The 2,400 million people speak about 2,800 different languages. Mandarin Chinese would probably win as the language spoken by the largest number of people; but English, with about 241 million speakers, makes a very respectable showing.

Probably the most significant way of classifying these people would be by "nationality," but goodness knows how many nationalities could be recognized in the world today. There are 60 member states in the United Nations, and there are a great many self-conscious nationalities in the world that haven't achieved independent national governments. I intend to look at this problem of the various ways of classifying people in a later chapter; here I want to examine not only the numbers of people now living on the globe, but also the past history of these populations.

I have emphasized the difficulties of making an accurate estimate of the present population of the world; these difficulties are great, and they increase enormously as we go back in time. The history of population has fascinated many scholars, however, and they have used great ingenuity in trying to arrive at likely estimates for the abundance of people in various parts of the world in past ages. It is clear that the great growth in numbers of people in most parts of the world is a recent phenomenon—but how recent? And what have been the actual rates of growth in different parts of the world?

The Constitution of the United States included provision for a complete enumeration of the population every ten years; and we can follow the growth of this country easily and accurately from the 3,929,214 inhabitants of the first census of 1790, to the 150,697,361 inhabitants counted in the most recent census of 1950. But there are few other parts of the world with comparable records. Sweden has the longest and most complete record. There, the local clergy had for a long time kept lists of their parishioners, and in 1749, the government required them to report in such a way that a total for the entire population could be obtained. This has been repeated at five-year intervals, providing an unusual, but very efficient method of following population history. The first official English census was taken in 1801, but the methods were defective, and demographers regard the census of 1841 as the first reliable one for that country.

We have, then, a certain number of fairly reliable records for Europe and North America from 1800 on to the present. As we go back in time, or move from Europe to Asia, Africa or Oceania, the estimates become ever more uncertain. Walter Willcox, the American statistician, made a thorough effort, in 1929, to evaluate all of the information that was available for population growth from 1650 on. Sir Alexander Carr-Saunders reviewed the Willcox figures in 1936 and made several modifications in the light of his broad knowledge of human population behavior. The Carr-Saunders figures have been widely accepted as about the most reasonable estimates possible with the information available, and they are given in the accompanying table, with the 1950 estimates added for comparison.

ESTIMATES OF WORLD POPULATION: 1650-1950 (*in millions*)

	1650	1750	1800	1850	1900	1950
EUROPE	100	140	187	266	401	559
ANGLO-AMERICA	1	1.3	5.7	26	81	166
LATIN AMERICA	12	11.1	18.9	33	63	162
OCEANIA & AUSTRALIA	2	2	2	2	6	13
AFRICA	100	95	90	95	120	198
ASIA	330	479	602	749	937	1302
WORLD TOTAL	545	728	906	1171	1608	2400

There may be errors of many millions in these figures, but no one doubts that they give a fair picture of the general trend of population growth for the world from about a half billion in 1650 to two and a half billion three hundred years later, a fivefold multiplication. The multiplication, furthermore, has been at an accelerating rate. From these figures, it would seem that the average increase every ten years in the seventeenth century was 2.7 per cent; in the first half of the eighteenth century, 3.2 per cent; in the second half of the eighteenth century, 4.5 per cent; in the nineteenth century, 5.3 per cent in the first half and 6.5 per cent in the second half; while in the present century, the population of the world has been increasing 8.3 per cent every ten years. No wonder students of population become alarmed when, from this immediate past, they look into the future! Three hundred years are but a minute out of the hundreds of thousands of years that man has been inhabiting this planet and reproducing his kind to the best of his ability. Any way you chart this, it looks like an explosion, and explosions are always frightening.

If we try looking at particular populations over these years, we can find every sort of variation. The Tasmanians may serve as one extreme: their population declined from about 5,000 in 1800, to zero in 1876, when the last survivor died. The other extreme may be the French Canadians: these number about four million now, practically all descended from some 5,800 immigrants who settled in Canada before 1680, when immigration from France ceased.

The Europeans have, in general, shown the greatest multiplication. In 1650, on their own continent, they included about 18 per cent of the world's population; by 1950, the European continent held 23 per cent of the world's total of people; and if the Europeans and their descendants in the Americas are added, this group has increased from a fifth of the world total in 1650, to a third of the total in 1950. From any cosmic point of view, the world seems to be faced with a "European white peril" rather than a "yellow peril." Yet the Asiatic peoples have almost held their own, including about half the world's population in 1950 as in 1650.

The figures show a decline and then a gain for the population of Africa. This could well be called a sheer guess, though a plausible one. African population has been a guessing game all along. Lord Hailey, in his African Survey, summarized the matter thus:

For the continent as a whole, estimates of 150,000,000 or more appeared in the eighteenth century; the evidence of explorers as to the relative emptiness of the countries they traversed resulted in a reduction of this figure to a range between 28,000,000 and 41,000,000 in the years between 1851 and 1868; the publication of Stanley's reports led to the adoption of figures up to 180,000,000 or more, that accepted in 1882 being as high as 205,000,000. Estimates made at various times since 1903 have varied between 126,000,000 and 149,000,000.

The differing estimates for African population have depended in part on what the estimator wanted to prove; whether attacking administrative and economic measures of colonial government or defending them in terms of their effect on native survival; whether supporting the boundless possibilities of Africa for human development, or showing the hopelessness of equatorial regions for the support of increasing populations. These differences become even more startling when comparisons are made between predictions of the future possibilities of Africa. Some students consider the continent already overpopulated; others calculate that its potential is enormous, that it might in the future support a billion or two billion people.

Carr-Saunders, after wading through this mass of conflicting evidence, decided that there was nothing to suggest an increase of population in any part of Africa before 1800. On the other hand, slave raiding and new diseases may have reduced the population so that, whatever it was in 1650, it was probably less in 1750 and still less in 1800. After 1800, the total population of the continent may have begun to increase: the population of North Africa (especially Egypt) certainly started to increase, but this may have been counterbalanced by a continuing decline in parts of tropical Africa. Since 1900, it is clear that there has been a general population increase in all parts of Africa. From a chain of reasoning of this sort come the figures so confidently set forth in the table on page 17.

Egypt would make a beautiful case for the study of the relation of population to economic and social conditions. At the time that it was the granary of the Roman Empire, the population was probably 8 million. When Napoleon arrived, 1800 years later, the population was estimated to be about 2½ million. The United Nations estimate for 1951 was a population of almost 21 million. Yet probably in each of these periods Egypt has looked overcrowded—has, in fact, been overcrowded. But that gets off into the question of the meaning of "overcrowding."

It is, then, possible to draw a reasonable and probable picture of the population growth of the world over the past three hundred years; at first only in very broad and general terms, but with increasing accuracy of detail in the nineteenth and twentieth centuries. But what was the situation before 1650?

Estimates for the world as a whole before the seventeenth century are so clearly guesses as to have little meaning. Population growth generally must have been slow, and with ups and downs differing greatly from one region to another—population increasing in one part of the world with peace and economic stability; decreasing in another as wars, famine and plagues afflicted disintegrating empires.

We can get some glimpse of the process in Europe. The whole course of development and decline of the Roman Empire was associated with considerable changes in populations, and many scholars have analyzed the surviving documents to find out what they could of the relations between the decline of the empire and the changing population situation. The empire, at the beginning of the Christian Era, is supposed to have had about 55 million inhabitants, of which 23 million lived in the European provinces. The regions beyond the confines of the empire were mostly sparsely peopled, so that the continent as a whole can have had only a few million more inhabitants. The population grew with the prosperity of the empire and declined with its disintegration to a low of perhaps 20 million people by A.D. 500. It is thought that the population grew slowly but steadily thereafter until the catastrophe of the Black Death, which first appeared in 1348 and which wiped out about a quarter of the population of Europe.

For Europe as a whole, then, we can imagine a population of perhaps 30 million in the time of Augustus, growing and then declining over the next five hundred years, growing again slowly until the onset of the medieval plagues, then finally recovering to reach 100 million by the seventeenth century. The over-all picture would be a threefold growth over these 1600 years, as compared with a fivefold growth over the next 300 years.

We can get quite definite information about medieval population at certain times and for limited areas. Two instances from English history may serve to illustrate this. The first instance involves William the Conqueror who commanded that an inventory be made of his new possession. This inventory, completed in 1086, was carried out in a thorough manner. The two great manuscript volumes reporting on the survey survive in the Public Record Office in England. This has come to be called the Domesday Book. A fourteenth-century clerk explained the name thus: "This book is called Domesday, that is, day of judgment, by metaphor for, just as the sentence of that last strict and terrible examination can be escaped by no art of tergiversation, so when a dispute shall arise in the kingdom touching words which are entered there, when recourse is had to the book, its sentence cannot be set at naught or declined with impunity."

A historian, Josiah Russell, has gone over the details of the Domesday Book very carefully, checking internal consistency and attempting to fill in various gaps—especially about the numbers of clergy and burgesses, who were not regularly recorded. He comes out with a total population for England in 1086 of 1,099,766 persons.

There is another reference point in the history of population in medieval England in the records of the poll tax of 1377. The king needed more money for the prosecution of the Hundred Years' War, and Parliament finally decided to impose a tax of fourpence (one groat) on every head in the kingdom, male or female, fourteen years of age and above. The collection of this tax seems to have been carried out with a thoroughness unusual in tax operations of that day. Russell, after checking the soundness of the tax returns in various ways, and making allowance for beggars and for other untaxed persons and for the probable number of children under 14 years of age, comes out with a population for England in 1377 of 2,232,373 persons. This represents a doubling of the population in the three hundred years between the Domesday Book and the poll tax. It seems to have about doubled again in the next 300 years to reach 4 million by 1650.

We can also get some idea of population growth in the non-European civilizations. Kingsley Davis has recently reviewed the evidence on the population history of India. He notes that between the seventh and fourth centuries B.C. the Buddhistic literature indicates that "the economy of northern India was comparable to that of the later middle ages in Europe. Crafts and commerce were flourishing and were highly organized. Money and credit were everyday instruments. The ordinary town seemed to embrace anywhere from 30 to 1,000 families, and approximately 20 cities existed in northern India alone." The records show that Chandragupta, about 300 B.C., maintained a standing army of about 700,000 men, the sort of army that could only be supported by a considerable population. Davis agrees with the estimates of Indian scholars, based on various lines of evidence from archeology, literature and history, that the population of India about 300 B.C. was between 100 and 140 million.

Davis estimates that the population in India in 1600 A.D., 2,000 years later, was about 125 million. In other words, there is good evidence that the population of India remained about the same—perhaps fluctuating between 100 and 140 million—for 2,000 years. There was no appreciable change until about 1850, when the modern spurt of Indian population growth started in earnest.

The evidence for all parts of the world indicates fairly stable, or only slowly changing, populations for the civilizations over the several thousand years between the Urban Revolution which, with its developments of techniques of food storage and transport, of craft specialization and the like, made cities and civilizations possible, and the Industrial Revolution, which marked the beginning of the present rapidly changing population situation. We can presume that there was a great increase in population during the period of the Urban Revolution, when the ancient civilizations were first developing, but we have no direct evidence on its rate or characteristics.

It is possible to get some idea of the numbers of peoples in these past civilizations. But what about the Neolithic farmers and gardeners who preceded them, or the "primitive" peoples who inhabited most of the world in historic times? The difficulty in arriving at figures for peoples under such circumstances are obviously enormous. For the most part, about the best we can do is observe the size of populations that can be supported by people living under primitive conditions at the present time, and assume that conditions in the past must have been similar. But

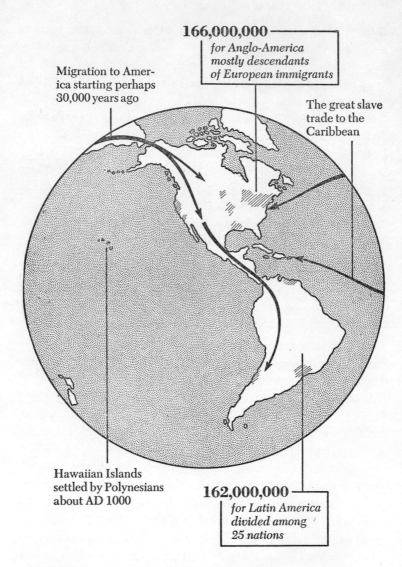

166,000,000
*for Anglo-America
mostly descendants
of European immigrants*

Migration to Amer-
ica starting perhaps
30,000 years ago

The great slave
trade to the
Caribbean

Hawaiian Islands
settled by Polynesians
about AD 1000

162,000,000
*for Latin America
divided among
25 nations*

PRESENT WORLD POPULATION &
GREAT HISTORIC MIGRATIONS

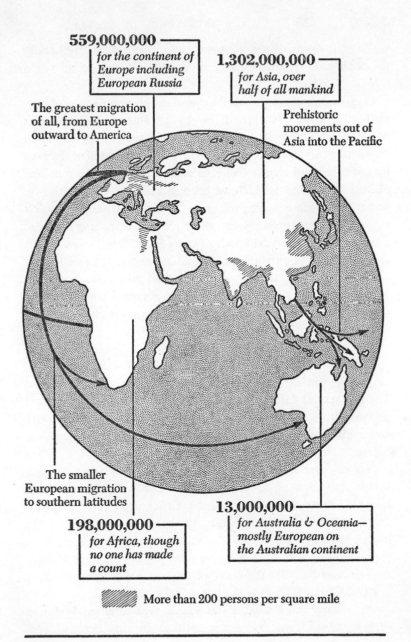

559,000,000 *for the continent of Europe including European Russia*

1,302,000,000 *for Asia, over half of all mankind*

The greatest migration of all, from Europe outward to America

Prehistoric movements out of Asia into the Pacific

The smaller European migration to southern latitudes

198,000,000 *for Africa, though no one has made a count*

13,000,000 *for Australia & Oceania— mostly European on the Australian continent*

More than 200 persons per square mile

we have, it seems to me, a great deficiency of information about the population relations of primitive peoples today, so that even this is difficult.

One of the most interesting studies of population of un-civilized people was carried out by an anthropologist, James Mooney, who attempted to determine the pre-European Indian population of North America. He compiled detailed lists of Indian tribes and checked various sorts of leads on the numbers of individuals that might have been included in each tribe. He had to deal with different tribes at the time that they were first encountered by explorers or settlers, which of course involved a time spread of several hundred years for different parts of the continent. But population conditions in general appeared to be fairly stable among the various tribes until they came in contact with the palefaces, so that the picture obtained with this time spread would probably be about the same as the picture in any single presettlement year—say 1500, or 1650.

Yet European influence did precede European observers. Horses and muskets got to the Great Plains before Europeans themselves got there; and after the first settlements, European diseases spread faster than the colonists. Such influences add obscurity to a picture that is already far from clear. But it still seems likely that the order of magnitude of Mooney's figures is correct.

Mooney arrived at the figure of 1,152,950 for the total pre-white population of America north of the Rio Grande. A. L. Kroeber, through a restudy of the California figures, reduced this to 1,025,950, with the remark that the total might be as low as 900,000. It probably also might be as high as 1,500,000, for all anyone knows. The figure generally adopted for 1650— the standard basis for the study of modern population growth— is 1,000,000.

The continental United States has an area of about 3 million square miles. If there were a million Indians here in pre-

European times, the density then would have been one person for every three square miles. Actually, the density was probably even less than this, since many of the million Indians were spread out thinly into the Canadian forests.

The Indians were partly in an agricultural stage of culture, partly in a hunting and gathering stage of culture. At a strictly food-gathering stage of culture, such as must have prevailed over much of man's evolutionary history, it takes about two square miles of fertile hunting territory to support each human individual. Since there are only about 20 million square miles of such land on our earth, the maximum possible population for the whole world in the Old Stone Age would have been about 10 million. Man may have reached some such figure a very long time ago, and remained at roughly those numbers through the tens of thousands of years of the latter part of the Pleistocene. His population may have been able to increase slowly as he discovered better ways of hunting or fishing or learned to exploit new plant foods, but surely there was no great change until he learned how to grow food. That was perhaps 10,000, perhaps 15,000 years ago.

We can see signs of local increases then in the village sites of Mesolithic and Neolithic times. But there is no evidence for really large numbers of people anywhere until the beginnings of the cities and the civilizations, four, five and six thousand years ago. The changes even then must have been very slow, at least as compared with the rate of change that we can document in the last few hundred years, since the onset of the newest change that we call the Industrial Revolution.

I want to look at the sequence of these changes in the next chapter, and especially at the older events of the Pleistocene, since it must have been these old events that formed our basic human nature—whatever we mean by that.

CHAPTER **3** THE NATURE OF MAN

Here is our world, then—a finite globe of continents and seas inhabited by some two and a half billion people living off the plants and animals of these continents and seas. Three hundred years ago it seems that there were only about a half a billion people living in the same space, on the same closed system of natural resources. Ten thousand years ago it is likely that these same resources were able to support, at the most, ten million people.

The basic resources, in terms of chemical elements, have not changed—there is the same amount of carbon, oxygen, sodium, and hydrogen; iron has been increased only by the amount of the occasional meteorites. The sun continues to pour energy into the system at the same basic rate.

Man, as a biological organism, has not changed—at least there have been no changes that we can detect. We have no trouble explaining human behavior within historic times in terms of drives and fears and hopes and motives that we find operating about us today. The bones, which are our only direct evidence of the nature of physical man, show the same structure and same variation ten thousand years ago as today. From this it seems likely that the muscles, guts and brains were also much the same. To find differences we must go back much further into time and start dealing with geological magnitudes.

The change in human numbers reflects not a change in the inherent nature of the resources, or in the inherent nature of the human animal, but a change in the relations between the two; a change in man's methods of dealing with the resources. In one vocabulary, we could call the change a matter of human economy; in another vocabulary, it is a change in culture. Whether we call it a change in "human nature" is perhaps a nice matter of definition.

We talk about human nature very glibly, mostly as a handy means of justifying some theory or action. Almost every imaginable kind of behavior has been explained by someone as a logical consequence of human nature; and damned by someone else as contrary to human nature—as "inhuman" or "unnatural"—until the term has come to lose all meaning.

The anthropologists have been particularly active in exploding the myth of human nature. They have shown that in some cultures it is perfectly "natural" to offer your wife to a guest as a gesture of hospitality; while in other cultures it is "natural" to go into a blind rage and kill both the wife and any male with whom she may be found in sexual contact. It is "natural" for some people to eat worms, and for other people to shudder at the idea. In fact, the search for universals has been almost fruitless—the "almost" being required by the apparent universality, for instance, of some form of incest taboo. But then you can still argue about whether an incest taboo is "natural" or not.

Yet, logically, there must be an underlying human nature, just as there is a cat nature, a raccoon nature, or what have you—a basic potentiality for behavior that finds its expressions in all of the diverse sorts of culture that we have been able to study. This basic potentiality might be called the instinctive equipment of the human animal. But the word "instinct" has been so badly misused that a great many psychologists have thought it better to abandon the word altogether and to frame their studies in some quite different vocabulary. They are still, however, looking for universals, for explanations of the peculiar behavior of that peculiar animal, man.

I think the peculiarities of man are most easily dealt with in terms of the anthropological word "culture." This might be defined as the sum of all human traits and activities that depend, for maintenance, on the various mechanisms associated with language—on speech and its derivatives, like writing, printing and mathematical formulation. Speech differs from the signal systems of animals because it depends on the use of symbols. How all this got started remains a puzzle.

There is no doubt now in the minds of scientists about the fact of human evolution, about the essential historical continuity between creatures that are clearly men and creatures that are clearly not men but apes or monkeys or some other kind of primate. How this evolution occurred, what forces governed it, what was the sequence of changes, is not so clear. Nor is there universal agreement about precisely where to draw the line between human and prehuman levels. Since we are dealing with a gradual and continuous series of changes, the precise point at which "prehuman" changes to "human" is surely arbitrary.

It is clear, however, that in studying the development of man, we have to deal with two sorts of processes—biological and cultural. We have to take into consideration not only biological evolution, but cultural evolution.

We study biological evolution in the biology classroom, learning that the amphibia first appear in the Devonian period, that the reptiles dominated the Mesozoic, giving way in the Cenozoic to the proliferating mammals. We can see, from the fossil record, the beautiful series of adaptive changes that occurred in the Miocene horses, and we can get a glimpse of the steps whereby certain primates, in the Pliocene and Pleistocene, changed from apelike to manlike form.

We study the physical basis of inheritance, whereby the characters of the parents are transmitted to the offspring through the chemical control of materials in the chromosomes; and we see how offspring may differ from parents through occasional shifts in this chromosome material, leading to variation within the species. We see how this pattern of inheritance can be governed through the forces of natural selection, leading to the survival of certain types of variation and the extinction of others, and how populations that become isolated from one another may follow diverging histories until presently there are two kinds of organisms where before there was one, and how, through hybridization and recombination, new swarms of variations may appear.

We pick up cultural evolution when we move from biology into anthropology or history. Our fossils here are the artifacts left by ancient man; we learn about Paleolithic and Neolithic stone tools, about Magdalenian cave paintings, about the development of metal working. We study the sequence of civilization in the valleys of the Nile, Euphrates and Indus rivers; we study the evolution of writing from pictographs through hieroglyphs to sound symbols, and the historical vicissitudes of the different alphabets. We follow the development of systems of government and religion among men. We are concerned with the transmission of ideas—with the origins of new ideas, the effect of contact between different idea systems, and with the occasional extinction of such systems.

There are many points of similarity between the two evolutionary processes, but there is also a fundamental difference.

The difference, I think, lies in the system of inheritance. Biological evolution depends on the continuity of the germ plasm; cultural evolution on the continuity of tradition. Biological inheritance is based in the chromosomes; cultural inheritance, in the language.

The possibility of speech is a product of biological evolution: it must have depended on the development of the vocal chords and of the appropriate brain centers in accordance with the same laws of evolution that led to the development of the human tooth structure or the human digestive system. And biological evolution has surely continued to operate on man, even though apparently swamped by this new system of cultural evolution. Communication through language may have started its modifying influence way back with "man-apes" and "ape-men" like Australopithecus or Pithecanthropus, getting its hold on the habits of man even before biological evolution had produced his present form. But as language communication developed, culture acquired a velocity of change quite unlike anything known in the prehuman world of organisms. We could probably hardly detect the change in the physical inheritance of a Magdalenian, a Mycenaean, a Greek, or a man today; but the cultural inheritance would, in each case, be vastly different.

This cultural inheritance is what takes the study of man out of the realm of ordinary biological methods. Man fundamentally is subject to biological laws just as is the mouse. Both the mouse and the man are also subject to the laws of the physicochemical universe; yet these laws do not serve in themselves to explain the mouse or man—something has been added with the factor of life. The mouse, perhaps, can be fully explained in terms of chemistry and biology, but this, for man, is still unsatisfactory, and we must study him not only in terms of his chemistry and biology, but also in terms of his culture.

This seems to be getting rather remote from the subject of population, but I think it is relevant to the understanding of the scientific approach to the study of any human problem. Biologists have been much concerned with the study of populations: with the laws that govern the fluctuations in the numbers of fruit flies in jars under given environmental conditions; with the laws that govern the periodic cycles of mice and rabbits and foxes under natural conditions; with the relation between the reproductive potential of different kinds of animals and the hazards of their existence and the availability of their food resources. Out of all of this we may hope to gain a constantly increasing understanding of the forces of biological evolution, and of the nature of the relations between the numbers of animals and the characteristics of their environment. Such studies are helpful in understanding the reproductive behavior of man, and the fluctuations in the numbers of men: but I do not think we can expect such studies ever to give us the whole answer, or by themselves, even to have much significance for human problems, until we have also taken into consideration the cultural factors that govern the numbers of men.

What I mean may be clearer if we stop to look at some of the factors governing the birth rate in men. The form and functioning of the sex organs are products of biological evolution. In studying the birth rate we must take into consideration the periodicity of ovulation in the female, and the phenomena of puberty and the menopause; we have the biological facts of the nine months' period of gestation, of the normal production of one young at a time, of the effect of breast feeding on succeeding ovulation. All such things are quite comparable in man and mouse, and may be studied similarly in the two species, and similarities and divergences noted in calculating the reproductive potential of the one as compared with the other.

But we cannot explain the actual birth rate of man in these biological terms. We have to look at the taboos and customs that hedge in sexual behavior; at differences in marriage customs which make age at marriage significant instead of age at puberty; we meet cults of virginity and of celibacy, or of prostitution; we find culture traits that lead to abortion or infanticide, or that block the biological sex function through contraception, or through other kinds of interference with plain, functional copulation. Mice may occasionally show bizarre behavior, especially when an experimental psychologist has had them in his hands for a while, but no mouse was ever subject to the variety of modifications of animal sex that confront every man—because no mouse has culture.

Biologists will sometimes argue about this—about culture being a peculiarity of man. Certainly endless examples of learning can be found among animals, and even of tradition, in which the learning is transmitted from parent to offspring, as with some elements of bird song. The biologists point out that the anthropologists are caught in a circular definition—man is distinctive because he has culture; culture, in turn, is defined as a characteristic of man.

In biological jargon, the two kinds of inheritance could be called "somatic" and "extrasomatic" from the Greek word *soma,* meaning "body." Clearly, man has no monopoly on extrasomatic inheritance. It turns up in all sorts of organisms— in the leaf-cutting ant that carries a tiny packet of fungus spores for starting the garden of a new nest, in many aspects of the behavior of social birds and mammals. But extrasomatic inheritance has become of overwhelming importance in man; it has come to dominate our behavior so completely that the difference can be considered, not merely a difference in amount, but a difference in kind.

Now cultural evolution takes place in a quite different frame of time from biological evolution. It seems to take, on the average, about a million years for a species, for a distinct kind of animal, to evolve; whereas cultures may change greatly in a few thousands or even a few hundreds of years. The changes, even so, sometimes seem terribly slow; and it is at least debatable whether we have or can have any conscious control over cultural changes or whether we are entirely the victims of impersonal forces.

Our knowledge of the details of either biological or cultural evolution is woefully scant—necessarily so from the nature of the fossil evidence. The biological fossils are mostly teeth and skull fragments, so that, with rare exceptions, it is impossible to be sure of the posture and size of the living creature. In no case can we be sure what early man looked like, because his looks would depend on soft parts, on muscle, skin and cartilage.

The cultural fossils are mostly stone tools. Yet surely from the beginning man has used stone for working wood or for killing game or making wars. There are complex cultures today which make almost no use of stone, and such cultures would leave no fossil traces. To try to reconstruct the way of life of a people, to guess what kind of shelters they made, what they ate, how they were organized into families and tribes, with only the stone tools to go on, is like trying to guess the facial expression from a fragment of jaw with only the second and third molar teeth in place.

Yet these stone tools can tell us much. Early man left a great many of them as clues to his presence and activity, and they have been intensively studied by many scholars. There is a rough sequence of development from the very crude earliest attempts at shaping stones for human use, to the smoothly polished tools of the New Stone Age. The artifacts found together in any particular place usually show a distinctive technique of manufacture. The various recognizable techniques are called "industries" by the archeologists, and each "industry" is given a name, usually after the place where it was first found. Thus we have the "Chellean industry," first described from gravel pits at Chelles-sur-Marne, characterized by a pick or hand axe formed by shaping a nodule of flint by knocking off flakes. Traces of this Chellean industry are widespread in Europe, and date from a very early period. It may be assumed that these Chellean implements correspond to some particular way of life that we can call the Chellean culture, and that this culture can be placed in space and time by the surviving relics of its industry.

The unraveling of time sequences involves nice detective work. Excavation in long inhabited places, like some of the European caves, yields series of industries neatly superimposed, with the oldest at the bottom; and occasionally some circumstance, like the deposit of a layer of a characteristic type of soil, enables the archeologists to make a tie-in from the industry sequence to the time scale of the geologists.

The history of stone-age industries has been most carefully worked out in Europe. This does not necessarily mean that Europe was particularly important in the cultural evolution of man; it may only mean that there have been more archeologists and geologists working in Europe than anywhere else.

Almost all of the evidence of human activity dates from the last of the geological periods, the Pleistocene. Stones called *eoliths* which competent observers consider to show definite signs of manipulation have been found in the preceding period, the Pliocene, but our knowledge of this Eolithic era, of this "dawning of culture," is scant indeed.

Modern geologists consider that the Pleistocene lasted for about a million years, and this seems time enough for the development of most cultural traits. The stone tools found over most of this period are classed as *Paleolithic,* as belonging to the Old Stone Age; and the term Paleolithic thus corresponds, in cultural history, to Pleistocene in geological history. The correspondence isn't complete, because the Old Stone Age gave way to the New Stone Age, the *Neolithic,* towards the end of the geological Pleistocene; but this Neolithic culture stage did not last for a tenth as long as the Paleolithic stage, so that it only comes in at the very last minute on the geological time scale, and passes over into time that the geologist dismisses as "recent," those last few seconds during which the conscious traditions of men and civilizations have developed.

The Pleistocene was short, as geological periods go, but it was also a queer period because of the odd changes that kept taking place in the earth's climate. Through most of its history, the earth seems to have been a relatively stable and equable place, but every once in a while there have been periods of violence, like the one we live in now, with crustal disturbance, mountain building, great erosion, and accumulation of polar ice. There are evidences of glaciation way back in geological time, but glaciation became a habit during the Pleistocene, and there is a succession of four distinct periods when polar ice slowly extended outward to cover, in the north, a good part of the continents of North America and Europe. Since man's biological and cultural evolution took place during these times of alternating glacial and interglacial periods, the whole matter of the climatic, faunal and geographical changes associated with glaciation becomes of great importance to students of man.

The last of the glacial periods is called the "Wisconsin glaciation" in the United States and the "Würm glaciation" in Europe. It probably started something like a hundred thousand years ago, and at its maximum the ice pretty well covered all of Canada, extending over the region of the Great Lakes down into Indiana and Ohio, and to Connecticut on the east coast. The ice in Europe was less extensive, but it covered all of Scandanavia, the Baltic and much of Great Britain, and there were large isolated glaciers in the Alps and Pyrenees. The glacial retreat was well under way 25,000 years ago, but the ice accumulation is still with us in Greenland and suchlike places, and it is probable that the earth's climates are now of a glacial, rather than an interglacial type. The shift from Paleolithic to Neolithic cultures took place during this last glacial retreat, and the sequence of human events both in Europe and North America is intimately related to the sequence of postglacial physical conditions.

These glaciers, at their maximum, represented the withdrawal of an enormous amount of water from normal circulation, and the level of the seas may have been lowered as much as 150 feet. A glance at any map giving ocean depths will show what a great shift this would mean in land relationships—in the outlines of Europe, or in connections with the continent and among the islands of the East Indies. Modern man was abroad all through this period, and his present distribution must reflect glacial as well as postglacial conditions.

Temperature and rainfall in the equatorial regions were probably little affected by this glaciation, but atmospheric circulation in the intermediate latitudes must have been greatly changed so that the present desert areas of these latitudes received sufficient rainfall to support vegetation—and man. This is borne out by direct evidence in the Sahara, for instance, and it is clear that human cultural changes in North Africa and the Near East were associated with these postglacial climatic changes; which is not the same thing as saying that the one is the result of the other. The climates in the vicinity of the glaciers would, of course, be very different from those prevailing in the same regions now.

In the accompanying table, I have tried to summarize the chronological relations between the glaciations of the Pleistocene, the succession of Paleolithic cultures, and the probable age of the various types of fossil men. Any such table represents a great oversimplification of the known facts, and makes other things that are at best reasoned guesses look as though they were facts. We don't know the exact time relations between Java man, Peking man, and so forth, or the relationships between any of these and the successive glaciations. But keeping all of that in mind, such a table may serve a useful purpose in general orientation.

We do have definite associations in many cases. We know,

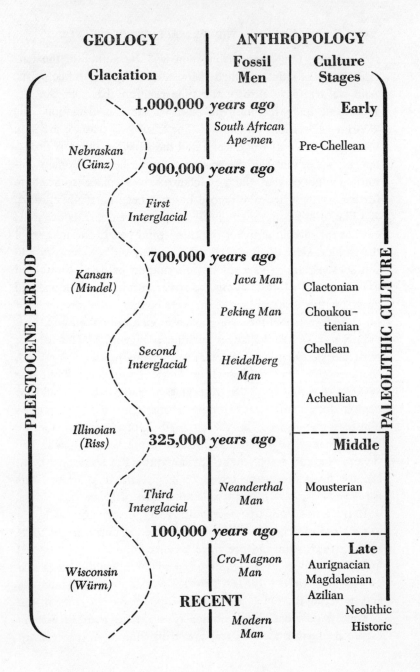

GEOLOGY | ANTHROPOLOGY

Glaciation | Fossil Men | Culture Stages

PLEISTOCENE PERIOD

PALEOLITHIC CULTURE

1,000,000 *years ago* — Early

Nebraskan (Günz)

South African Ape-men — Pre-Chellean

900,000 *years ago*

First Interglacial

700,000 *years ago*

Kansan (Mindel)

Java Man — Clactonian

Peking Man — Choukou-tienian

Second Interglacial

Chellean

Heidelberg Man

Acheulian

Illinoian (Riss)

325,000 *years ago* — Middle

Third Interglacial

Neanderthal Man — Mousterian

100,000 *years ago*

Late

Wisconsin (Würm)

Cro-Magnon Man — Aurignacian Magdalenian Azilian

RECENT

Neolithic Historic

Modern Man

for instance, that Neanderthal man was the author of the particular type of industry called "Mousterian" by the archeologists. And we are fairly sure of the time relations between the late Paleolithic industries and the onset of the last glaciation (the "Würm" glaciation) in Europe. The trouble is that we are sure of such details only for Europe and the Mediterranean region—and I suspect that Europe was on the periphery of human cultural evolution, that the key changes took place somewhere further south, where the record has not been carefully studied.

I like to think that many basic human developments are most easily explained in terms of the trade-wind belt of the margin of the tropics. Here there is a climatic alternation between dry and wet seasons, and a vegetational alternation between forest and grassland: with forests along the rivers and in the hollows, and grass on the drier uplands. In such country, the products of both the forests and the savannahs are open to exploitation, providing a series of challenges to human ingenuity. The forests, particularly, provide a rich variety of plant products for food, shelter, tools, and medicinal or magical purposes; while the savannahs support a huge reservoir of game which could be exploited by man because of his upright posture, which gives him reasonable speed and yet leaves his hands free, and because of his capacity for social organization into a hunting pack. The savannah game would make difficult prey for a solitary man; but for ingenious man, acting cooperatively in a group, this game provides a rich and available source of food.

It is easiest, too, to understand man's association with fire in such savannah country, because in such country, in all parts of the world, man and fire have become practically a "natural force," as important in shaping and maintaining the landscape as rain and wind. Fire in a forest is a calamity, as dangerous and terrifying to man as a volcanic eruption; but a savannah fire is quite a different thing, obviously useful to man in driving game, in opening the landscape, and in stimulating the growth of fresh, tender grass. It is easy to visualize man accidentally producing fire by chipping flints in a dry savannah—and realizing that the accident was useful instead of disastrous.

The clues of geology and archeology all indicate that Paleolithic man had an economy of food-gathering and hunting. He exploited rather than manipulated nature. When he started to shift this economy, to cultivate plants and domesticate animals, he also started on new methods of tool-making, and we name the changed economy after the changed technique and call it Neolithic—the New Stone Age. The change, viewed with the perspective of those million years of Pleistocene time, appears quite sudden; and we find a variety of artifacts—new tools, pottery, aggregations indicating the construction of villages—that suggest how complete was the change in the way of life. But this cultural transformation into Neolithic man—this change from food-gatherer to food-producer—was based on a human nature that had been shaped by primarily biological forces acting through the long period of Paleolithic culture. In the few thousand years that have passed since the beginning of the Neolithic revolution, there has hardly been time for drastic modification of man's biological inheritance as shaped in those million years of the Pleistocene. So, if we want to understand ourselves, we shall do well to try to learn as much as we can from the fragmentary records that man has left of his Paleolithic period, because this is the basis on which the whole subsequent overgrowth of culture has formed.

There are a few deductions that can be made directly from the archeological record. When we find bones carefully split open, the only plausible explanation is that man was getting at the marrow to eat—other animals might gnaw the bones, but they would not be capable of splitting them. When we find human bones split open, we then can deduce that man was eating man. Since such split bones occur way back in the Stone Age, it looks as though cannibalism were an old human trait.

When we find burials in which the skeleton is accompanied by tools and ornaments, we can assume some sort of belief in an afterlife. When there are two skeletons together, apparently buried at the same time, one of a male and the other of a female, it looks like some sort of *sati* with the wife sent to accompany her master into the beyond—and a further deduction might be made about women being subordinate in the society. The skeleton of an older man accompanied by one or several other male skeletons may indicate slavery, with slaves being included along with other grave furnishings. Very imposing or especially rich graves may indicate chiefs.

Such complexities start showing up rather late (in geological time) and especially characterize the Mesolithic, the transition from the Old Stone Age to the New. In the Neolithic the evidence for cultural evolution begins to multiply, with remains of houses and villages, with pottery and later metal objects added to the list of cultural "fossils." Such evidence is especially useful in trying to understand the later stages of cultural evolution, the changes between "barbarism" and "civilization." With civilization we begin to get monuments and writing and ever more complete documentation.

This historical approach to the understanding of human nature, of biological and cultural evolution, provides us with a slender, but necessary, frame around which to build our theories. To fill out details and to gain much understanding, we must resort to the comparative method, to the study of the wide variety of differing cultures that survive into our own time.

There are many dangers in the comparative approach to the study of evolution, cultural or biological. No present culture is "ancestral" to any other living culture, just as no living species of animal is ancestral to any other living species. The Australian blackfellows of today have a culture based on tools that are similar to the tools surviving from the Paleolithic, and in that sense it can be called a Stone Age culture. But glaciers have waxed and waned, time has passed, for the Australian culture as well as for ours, and we cannot assume that the Australian culture has remained unchanged while ours has evolved. The changes have surely been in different directions; changes have probably also been at different "rates" if we could figure out a measure for rate of culture change.

But we can learn a great deal from the Australians, from the comparative approach to culture study, if we keep this qualification firmly in mind, and if we make sure that our deductions and conclusions are in line with the few facts that we have from the direct record of history, our cultural fossils.

The comparative method is especially useful in the study of population. We can see, from the geological and archeological evidence, a general sequence of economy, from the food-gathering economy of Paleolithic time, to the food-producing economy that came in with Neolithic, with consequent changes in man's relations with the rest of nature. We can get some idea of the conditions of existence in a food-gathering economy by studying the living peoples who still have such an economy. By looking at the wide variety of practices in agriculture and animal husbandry that survive in various cultures, we can get some idea of what may have been comparable practices in past times.

Unfortunately, we can never be sure, and on some of the most crucial points we get very little information. Because the Australians are food-gatherers, we cannot assume that their social organization is similar to that of Paleolithic man in Europe or anywhere else. The fact that the Australians practice infanticide doesn't prove that infanticide was a general characteristic of food-gathering groups, and so on through the whole catalogue of social characteristics.

When we find a characteristic, such as infanticide, to be widespread among different kinds of cultures, and to be prevalent among the surviving food-gathering cultures, it is possible, perhaps even probable, that the practice is an ancient one; but that is about as far as we can go in the absence of direct evidence from the past. For cannibalism we have such evidence, but we still don't know whether cannibalism was once general, or whether, as in recent times, it occurred in some cultures and not in others.

We are faced with these great uncertainties when we try to unravel the development of family and clan relations, or warfare and other kinds of intrahuman antagonisms, and when we try to get some light on the origins of food habits and sex habits and other customs of crucial importance from the point of view of population history. I don't see why the uncertainty should stop us from speculating—as long as we remember that the product is speculation—and I expect to indulge in speculation on the history of human traits at many points in this book.

Of one thing we can be sure, from both historical and comparative studies: that human nature is a relatively plastic affair, capable of modification in many directions. The two and a half billion specimens of man presently inhabiting our planet show an extraordinary variety in both biological and cultural inheritance—from which one might deduce that with man, almost anything is possible for the future as for the past.

The best way of emphasizing this variety may be through a glance at some of the ways in which men have been classified.

CHAPTER 4 THE KINDS OF MAN

No two of the two and a half billion living men are alike. Identical twins come closest—coming from a single egg that split in two after fertilization, identical twins have identical genetic constitutions. They are also generally treated almost alike after birth, so that they tend to have similar experiences; but the experiences are never completely identical; and close friends, at least, can recognize differences in the resulting personalities.

With the exception of these identical twins, it seems likely that no two humans who ever lived have had the same genetic constitution. The possible combinations of human genes run to many millions of millions, and the few thousands of millions of men who have so far come into existence represent only a small fraction of these possibilities. When we combine the biological variability with the cultural variability, the diversity becomes staggering.

45

Yet there is a certain order in the diversity. No two people are alike, but some people are more alike than others; and they may be alike in various sorts of ways—in appearance, personality, age, ability, or what-have-you. In order to study this variability, we have to attack the problem of classifying it, of finding an expression for whatever orderly relationships may exist.

It would be interesting to try to make a survey of all of the different ways in which men have been classified; but this would be an immense undertaking. Some of the classifications have been simple—Greeks and barbarians, Christians and heathen, freemen and slaves. Other classifications, however, have been both complex and subtle. Our interest here is in classifications that have been used in studying populations—but the subject is diverse enough even with this limitation. Studies of population rarely deal with mankind as a whole; they deal with Frenchmen, coal miners, Arabs, farmers, Negroes, New Yorkers, school children, criminals, or some other category in some kind of a classificatory system. Any such list obviously contains quite different sorts of categories, some based on nationality, others on race, or religion, or occupation, or age.

Let's look at race first. So much has been written about this that it seems criminal to add to the verbiage. I'll at least try to be brief. The trouble, of course, is that the description and classification of human physical types has got almost hopelessly blurred by emotional considerations. We are hardly able to distinguish between this race and that without getting involved with questions as to whether this race is "better" than that—brighter, more advanced, or nearer to the angels.

Some people would like to abandon the word "race" altogether and substitute a more neutral term like "ethnic group." But this flight from words is a losing game because the objectionable connotations catch up so rapidly. We can see this with the history of words for excretory products and places to deposit them. We invent a nice expression, but as soon as it gets generally established, the niceness starts to wear off and we have to invent a new expression. I had rather avoid the whole process, keep away from rest rooms and powder rooms and go back to Anglo-Saxon—but my wife objects. At least, I can cling to "race."

It still may be difficult to give race any precise meaning: but this perhaps is part of the problem, that we mistakenly try to use a general and vague term specifically and with precision. We are trying, with race, to describe the geographical variability of human physical traits. Now this geographical variability is a real thing, not only with man, but with a great many other organisms, particularly with land mammals. Populations that are partly or wholly isolated by geographical barriers of one sort or another—including mere distance—tend to follow divergent evolutionary paths and thus, with the passage of time, to become more and more different. The tendency to become different may be counterbalanced in varying degree by mixture among the populations, which makes an opposite tendency toward uniformity. No surviving populations of men have been sufficiently isolated for a long enough time to have evolved into recognizably distinct species; but many populations have been isolated enough to allow the development of considerable differences.

There is rather general agreement about the main stocks— Negroid, Mongoloid and Caucasian—and these show a general geographical pattern with the Negroid centering in Africa; the Caucasian in Europe, the Near East and India; and the Mongoloid in the Far East and America. Endless subdivisions can be made within each of these basic divisions. Carleton Coon, for instance, in his detailed study of the *Races of Europe,* finds ten main racial types among European Caucasians, each with various subtypes. All of these, of course, are abstractions, but they are made in an effort to describe a diversity that is real.

The main racial stocks all blend into one another completely, so that no arbitrary line can be drawn between any two of them. And then there are various populations that don't fit any of the main types—especially some of the dark-skinned peoples of the Pacific. The Australian blackfellows, too, are different enough perhaps to be listed as a fourth main type, though they may be classed as "Negroid" on skin color alone, or as a "primitive White type" if attention is paid to other traits, such as hair.

The trouble is that man has been in a state of flux for a long time, with races emerging or disappearing or blending as populations remained stationary and isolated or got involved with migratory shifts. We can see the process of race formation now in Hawaii. A new but recognizable type (the "Neo-Hawaiian") seems to be emerging there from the mixture of Mongoloid and European peoples with the local Polynesians. The Polynesians in turn probably emerged as a recognizable type from a mixture of antecedent types somewhere in southeast Asia a few thousand years ago. And the process can thus be projected back in time as an alternation of mixing and isolating, hybridizing and segregating, pressures. The problem of dealing with race is the problem of dealing with a dynamic process, of describing particular cross sections in time and space through a system in flux.

One of the curious things about this race business is that while a considerable variety of physical types can be fairly well described and defined, attempts to show differences in behavior and physiology that correspond to these physical types have been generally unsuccessful. Because of this, race is not a very meaningful term in population study.

There are, to be sure, broad correlations between population behavior and race, such as the great multiplication and spread of the Caucasian type during the last three hundred years, the relative stability of the African Negro populations, and the trend toward extinction of many racial types such as the Australian and the Polynesian. But these trends are all understandable, not in terms of race but in terms of culture; and race and culture behave generally as independent variables.

It is true that Western civilization, which has been the aggressive and dominant culture of the last three hundred years, is primarily the culture of the Caucasian people of Western Europe. Attempts to explain this culture in terms of racial characteristics of these peoples, however, have not been very convincing. At least they fail to explain why European Caucasians remained in a barbarian stage while other racial types were building dominant and aggressive civilizations. They fail to explain the ease with which in some cases other races, such as the Mongoloids represented by the Japanese, have picked up and used Western cultural elements. The whole situation is much more understandable in terms of geographical distribution of resources, and the interplay of historical, cultural and economic factors; and neither racial mentality nor racial physiology need be brought into the explanation at all.

The use of the racial terms "White" and "Negro" in the United States is interesting in this regard. The population of the United States clearly has three quite different geographical (and racial) origins: the local American Indians, and the immigrants from Europe and tropical Africa. Cultural forces in the United States have tended to maintain the distinctness of these groups, so that the mixing has not been as thorough as in other countries (like Brazil and Honduras) where somewhat different cultural forces have been in operation. But even so there has been a great deal of mixing, so that it is difficult to be sure that any individual is of purely African, Indian or European descent. (Who can keep track of all of his ancestors for, say, ten generations? And remember that Prince Henry of Portugal started raiding the African coast back in 1441, and sold the captured slaves all over Europe.)

"White" and "Negro" are commonly used categories in population studies in the United States, but I can't see that this usage has much to do with race. All sorts of statistical differences can be found between the two groups, but the differences seem to reflect economic rather than racial characteristics. Individuals listed as "Negro" may have more Europeans than Africans in their immediate ancestry, which doesn't make sense to me. If we were really interested in race, surely the way to make the separation would be between people with a preponderance of Europeans in their immediate ancestry and people with a preponderance of Africans—though how one would determine this, I don't know.

I agree with the people who maintain that race is a meaningless term as it is currently used in the United States—but this is not saying that it is a meaningless term under all circumstances. It is most useful as a biological concept. But the determining factors of group differences in human behavior—including population behavior—seem to be cultural rather than biological.

Actually, the most meaningful units in population analysis are political—nations, empires and colonies. The statistics, of course, are gathered according to political units by the various governments, which might tend to give a spurious sort of reality to the units surveyed. But the influence of the national state has become so pervasive in the modern world that we cannot doubt its reality. Only with great difficulty can we generalize about population trends among different races because the trends are the product, not of racial characters, but of cultural forces that find expression within political units. Our most important classification, then, is not into whites and blacks, but into English, French, Japanese, Chinese, Americans (in the restricted sense), Mexicans, and so forth.

The more you think about this, the more curious it seems. The national state, historically, is a recent invention. The whole idea is sometimes blamed on the French Revolution and subsequent Napoleonic adventures. "Italy" and "Germany" did not appear on the scene as nations until 1870. To be sure, many nations, like France and England, have had long histories of national sovereignty over areas closely similar to their present boundaries, but this seems not so much a "natural" phenomenon as a result of a series of geographical and historical accidents.

No national state corresponds to a racial grouping. Israel may be attempting to unite the two, but no anthropologist can distinguish Jews in any racial sense. Some nations are fairly homogeneous racially, but they represent at most a piece of that particular racial stock, with the rest scattered among other nationalities.

"National character" has lately become a perfectly respectable subject for anthropological study. The concept of the Englishman, the American or the German seems to be just as real as the concept of some racial type, or some tribal culture. We tend to think of the American melting pot as a rather special phenomenon; and it is, since the other national characters are rarely smelted from such a diversity of materials. But the other national characters are thus, perhaps, all the more easily shaped.

The political frontier, as every traveler knows, is a very real element of geography. Often it is much more difficult to cross than a river, a mountain range, or a desert. These frontiers thus bound population isolates—define populations more sharply than most "natural" boundaries. Where the frontiers are drawn right across populations that were previously united, as has happened in Europe, governments have sometimes managed large population transfers to speed up and consolidate the isolating effect of the frontier. That, I suppose, is the answer to the reality of national character—the omnipotence and reality of governments, with the power to direct and control many of the forces that shape a culture. Though, of course, there is the opposite theory, that the government is the product of the culture, of the national character.

At any rate, population studies generally deal with national units and their political appendages; and these differ enough from one another to make it clear that the political units are something more than statistical conveniences. Countries with similar cultural and economic developments tend to show similar population trends, so that we can often generalize about Western Europe, Latin America, Southeast Asia, and the like. National differences within such groupings may still be considerable, however, as with France, England, Ireland, the Netherlands and Italy.

The explanation of these national differences is surely complex and subtle, involving educational systems, religious attitudes, economic development, public health policy, political history and the like. We shall necessarily have to take a look at many of these things, insofar as they are related to population developments, in later parts of this book.

National states inevitably form the basic frame for any discussion of the population developments of contemporary man. They are also neat and convenient units for such discussion because they are sharply defined. You can always tell, by consulting the atlas, where one ends and another begins. This changes, of course, with the vicissitudes of wars and treaties, but such changes are at least well advertized. The national states, however, despite the most earnest efforts of their governments, are not uniform affairs. There are, in every state and every colony, many different possible classifications of the inhabitants, and any understanding of national trends usually requires analysis in terms of such subsidiary classifications.

I am thinking now particularly of the division into social or economic classes. We have had visions of a classless society before us now for some time, but no one seems to have figured out a practical way of achieving this or, once achieved, of making it work—though revolutionaries have sometimes managed a thorough job of replacing one class structure with another. Thus, whether we deplore class systems or not, they are certainly with us, and proper subjects for study. And class structure is involved in population analysis since, in the modern West at any rate, family size is definitely related to social or economic position.

The sociologists have become much concerned with the description and analysis of social stratification, and have studied it from many different points of view. The easiest way of breaking a population into classes is by means of some readily determined criterion, such as family income, years of education of parents, or occupation of father. This is not very satisfactory in some ways, however, because the importance of the divisions depends not so much directly on income, occupation and education, as on social interactions which lead to the development of group opinion, group sanction of some activities, and group prohibition of others.

One of the best-known studies of this problem was made by Lloyd Warner and various associates in a New England town which they called "Yankee City." They carried out a careful survey of who visited whom and of what different people thought of the social position of other people. By this means they arrived at a division of six social classes, which they called "upper-upper, lower-upper, upper-middle, lower-middle, upper-lower and lower-lower." The upper-upper were clearly upper crust, sometimes without much money now, but definitely with lots of ancestors; people of this group not only thought well of themselves, they were well thought of by the rest of the community; and the lower-uppers, at least, were always trying to break into the upper ranks, and sometimes succeeding. The lower-lowers, at the other extreme, were definitely bums; and if they didn't know it themselves, everyone else did. In this community of 16,785 people, only 242 were classed upper-uppers, with 262 lower-uppers almost making the grade. There were 1,715 upper-middles, 4,720 lower-middles, 5,471 upper-lowers, and 4,234 lower-lowers.

It is easy to make fun of this. John Marquand, in his *Point of No Return,* did a beautiful job of describing the social scientists at work in this particular town—and of describing the problems of the scientist in trying to study the system instead of accepting it and becoming part of it. But the scientists are groping toward something that is real enough. The reality comes through Marquand's satire, and everyone of us has felt it in his own life.

Evidently the classes represent, in a sense, subcultures, with attitudes and habits that are sometimes strikingly different from one another even in the democratic and mobile society of the United States. Kinsey, in his famous study of our sex habits, has used years of education as an index of class differences; and he has found that both sex attitudes and sex habits differ considerably among the grammar school, high school, and college educated. He does not feel that this is a direct result of the extent of education, but only that education is a convenient guide to social class for his purposes. Direct social ranking, like that used by Lloyd Warner, would be impractical in a nationwide statistical study because of local variability of class structures and because such ranking requires the careful evaluation of many lines of evidence and becomes an end in itself. It is thus rarely possible to carry out demographic or population studies directly in terms of class.

The class structure of a society, however, has probably always been an important element in the population behavior of the society, though we have clear statistics on this only for the modern West. The modern West, I suspect, is exceptional in the kind of behavior it has shown; but since it is the most clearly documented, we may look at it first.

In general, in the modern West, family size increases as one goes from upper to lower in the social scale. The very upper crust may present an exception to this, but its members are generally too scarce in any particular study to provide good statistics. This upper crust tends to be conscious of its virtues, and with the spread of the eugenics idea, its members have sometimes felt a conscious obligation to perpetuate these virtues with large families—where their income was also large enough to be able to afford it.

But in general, the higher the social position, the smaller the family. A. B. Hollingshead, in a study of a middle-western town which he called "Elmtown," found that the few members of the top class (Class I in his system) had only one or two children per family. I suspect that Hollingshead's "Class I" would correspond to Warner's "lower-upper," since really upper-uppers in the New England sense become rare except in large cities as one goes inland from the Atlantic seaboard. At any rate, in Class II of this middle-western town, the average was 2.3 children per family; in Class III, 3.6; in Class IV, 4.3; and in Class V, 5.6. The bums, in other words, were the most prolific.

The Elmtown study was made in 1941 and 1942, and most such studies were made before the "baby-boom" after World War II. No one is really sure yet about the size of postwar families; though young wives of all classes are now having babies at a rate that gives jitters to authorities who will later be responsible for educating them.

In general, as I said, it has been impractical to make studies of reproduction directly in terms of social status. It is easier to use occupation, education or income as a rough index to the social structure. The most convenient way of comparing fertility among such groups is in terms of the number of births per year per thousand wives of childbearing age.

A 1935 study by Clyde Kiser of "native-white, urban families" showed that wives of unskilled workers had a birth rate of 115 births per thousand wives; of skilled workers, 100 births; of business men, 86 births; and of professional men, 94 births. The same study showed a similar correlation with the education of the wife. Births among wives who had had less than seven grades of schooling averaged 118 per thousand; wives who had reached the seventh or eighth grade averaged 105 births per thousand; among wives with high school education, the average was 91 births; with college education, 87 births.

In terms of family income, wives in families on total relief averaged 147 births per thousand; in families with incomes below $1,000 the average was 117 births; with incomes between $1,000 and $1,500, 90 births; with incomes between $1,500 and $2,000, 81 births; and with incomes of $2,000 or more, 76 births. Above $2,000, the drop in birth rate with increase in income ceased to be significant. ($2,000 was a lot more money in 1935 than in 1955.)

Studies of population trends within the various nations of Western Europe give results similar to those found in the United States, though with considerable differences in details. The present situation, of highest reproduction in the lowest social strata, is perhaps temporary. It has prevailed for only about three generations and it seems clearly to be a reflection of the adoption of contraceptive practices first by the better educated and wealthier members of the society. There is a certain amount of evidence that this difference between classes is becoming less as birth control measures become widespread. In the city of Stockholm, for instance, the trend has already reversed; and people with the lowest incomes have the fewest children; those with the highest incomes, the most children.

Until recently, the effect of the class structure on population has probably been through mortality rather than through fertility. Studies made a hundred years ago showed that the less favored economic groups had a strikingly higher mortality than the more favored. In Liverpool in 1842, for instance, a study showed that the average length of life of individuals in the working classes was 15 years; among the gentry, 35 years. Poor and inadequate food, crowded living conditions, poor sanitation, caused very high death rates, especially for infants, among the poor as compared with the more wealthy.

The lot of the city poor in the first half of the nineteenth century was perhaps unusual. Infant death rates in the cities of the United States and England climbed steadily during this period, even though death rates for the population at large were dropping. But while growing industrialization and urbanization may have aggravated the differential mortality of social classes, the differential has been with us for a long time—is still with us, in fact.

Demographers have long been preoccupied with population differences between the city and the country, between urban and rural environments. In social terms, this perhaps involves singling out one or two classes—farmers and farm laborers—and comparing them with all of the rest. One might also debate the meaning of "rural." It has got a special significance in the United States because of our system of dispersed farms on which the farmers live; but in much of the world and over much of history, farmers have lived in villages and walked out to their fields to work, which makes for a quite different social environment.

Even so, there is a curious characteristic of the city which seems in all ages and all regions to have led to a lowered rate of reproduction. Mortality has perhaps often tended to be higher in cities than in the country, because of the increased hazards of disease; but fertility has also tended to be lower. It has been asserted that the great city has never reproduced itself, but has always depended on immigration from surrounding territory, in ancient Egypt or China as in the modern West.

The city has always provided diversions for its population, so that they perhaps have not pursued sex with the single-mindedness of rural people. And the city has always provided such institutions as prostitution, so that sex need not necessarily be reproductive. I have often wondered, though, whether beyond such things there may not also be a physiological effect of the stress and tempo of city life that lowers fecundity so that man in the city, like so many animals in the zoo, becomes relatively infertile.

The great cities are a curious and fascinating case of human population behavior, in which social stratification and differentiation has reached its maximum. They are, however, a special case, and perhaps we should look at the general problem of the evolution of social categories, of the evolution of social structure within populations. The hazards of life, the prospects of marriage, the availability of food, and consequently reproduction and mortality, have probably always differed for slaves, serfs, nobles, knights, scribes and peasants. How did such differentiation come about?

We can assume that complex social stratification did not start until after man had shifted from food-gathering to food-producing, and started to live in ever larger population aggregates. But were the rudiments of a hierarchy always present in human social organization? In the food-gathering bands of the Pleistocene, was there a leader or chief, who was able, among other things, to gather more wives than other males in the group, and thus reproduce more prolifically?

The fossil record is of no help here. There are no indications of chieftainship until quite late, when special graves begin to appear; but this is no proof that the chieftainship idea was a late one. The comparative study of contemporary societies is also disappointing. By a judicious sifting of the reports of anthropologists and travelers, it is possible to find support for almost any theory of the origin of social hierarchy. The first-hand accounts themselves have perhaps been colored by the European feeling that every group or tribe must have a chief. Certainly both the idea of chieftainship and of some sort of social hierarchy are widespread. But it seems clear also that they are not universal.

During recent years biologists have given considerable attention to the study of "social hierarchy" or "peck-order" among mammals. Some sort of a social structure seems to be almost universal among social vertebrates, and thus may well have characterized primitive man. It seems to me highly probable that man was a social animal before he became a bearer of culture, because I cannot imagine how culture, how systems of symbolic communication, could have arisen except in a social animal.

The peck-order idea started with the studies of the behavior of chickens made by a Norwegian named Schjelderup-Ebbe. Who pecks whom, in a chicken run, turns out to depend on a fixed hierarchy determined early in the history of a particular flock. Schjelderup-Ebbe extended his studies to other types of flocking birds, and found the peck-order to be universal. This convinced him that despotism was a major biological principle. "Despotism," he wrote, "is the basic idea of the world, indissolubly bound up with all life and existence. On it rests the meaning of the struggle for existence." Which is a pretty broad flight to make with a flock of chickens.

Studies of mammals, and especially social primates, are more to the point as far as human nature is concerned. Here, too, most students have found a social hierarchy which gives the advantage in reproduction to dominant males. The trouble is that most of the monkey and ape studies have been carried out under caged conditions—which is a little like generalizing about human behavior from observations on a well-run concentration camp.

Our only really detailed study of the behavior of social monkeys under natural conditions was carried out by C. R. Carpenter, on howler monkeys in Panama. Carpenter practically lived with these monkeys for a year, snooping around through the forest, rain or shine, trying to get all of the details of their private lives. His results give no support to the theory that social hierarchy is a part of the "natural" order of things. The howlers, certainly as highly social as any living primate, seem to get along perfectly well without special leaders.

Carpenter writes:

Howler males behave in a communal manner when leading a clan. In conditions where there is a network of arboreal pathways or a lack of clearly defined routes, much exploratory "random" seeking behavior is shown. Each male of the clan participates, as a rule, in this exploratory behavior. In novel situations, one animal does not set off in a given direction with the rest of the clan and the other males following in sheep fashion. Prior to progression, every male may actively explore, move here and there, follow a route for a short distance, and then return to the clan. When a male finds a suitable route, he will give the deep clucking vocalization; then the females and young begin to follow him slowly, and associated males cease their exploratory behavior and fall in line with the moving column of animals.

Carpenter did not observe any instances of fighting among the males forming a part of the particular clan. As far as sex was concerned, the initiative seemed to be entirely with the females. A female in heat would approach a male, apparently any male who happened to be convenient, and induce him to copulate with her; then move on to some other male when the first one lost interest. As Carpenter said, "Howler males have not been observed to compete for sexually receptive females, for food, or for position."

It seems to me perfectly possible that the social evolution of man started from some prehuman social organization like that of the howlers. I must admit, though, that when one observes the maneuvering of children in the schoolroom or on the playground, or the interaction of adults at cocktail parties or in committee meetings, the behavior seems more similar to that in a chicken run than to that in a howler clan. But this pecking behavior may be a secondary development, characteristic of competitive societies like our own, because certainly the anthropologists have described societies which seem to be much less concerned than ours with prestige and competition, and that yet function smoothly as social units.

The nature of the culture and the differences among cultures play such an overwhelming role in the determination of many aspects of human behavior that perhaps we should have dealt with the kinds of culture before looking at the kinds of man. Cultures, however, are generally classified in economic terms— as food-gathering, agricultural, pastoral, industrial and the like —and from this point of view the cultural systems can be looked at as interposed between the animal man and his food supply, his means of subsistence. These relations between man and the means of subsistence will be the subject of the next chapter.

In this present chapter we have taken a very superficial look at only three kinds of classification of men—biological, political and social in the senses of race, nation and class. These, perhaps, are the most useful classifications from the population point of view; but all of the other ways in which men have been classified have some relevance to population, too. The attempts to group men into physical types—fat and lean; athletic, asthenic and pyknic; or in the latest terminology of W. H. Sheldon, endomorphs, mesomorphs and ectomorphs—have been completely ignored. And we have neglected some of the most fascinating studies of all, the attempts to describe and classify the varied personality types that we see among our friends and enemies. Psychology, sociology and anthropology have pooled their resources in many of these studies to form one of the most active growing points in the science of man.

But our present concern is not with the variety of people directly, but with the prevalence of people, which, Malthus said, was controlled by their means of subsistence.

CHAPTER *5* THE MEANS OF SUBSISTENCE

Concern about the "population problem" can be rather neatly dated from the year 1798, when a small book was published anonymously in London with the title *An Essay on the Principle of Population as It Affects the Future Improvement of Society*. The book immediately aroused discussion and controversy. The criticisms spurred the author to further work, and in 1803, Thomas Robert Malthus dropped anonymity and published a second edition, which was really a new book, much longer and more carefully documented than the first edition, and with a considerable change in emphasis. Four further editions were published in Malthus' lifetime, but with only slight revision and addition; the second edition of 1803 remained the basic statement of the Malthusian theories.

Among the contemporaries of Malthus, more people talked

about the book than read it, though six editions must have meant that a considerable number of copies were in circulation. The book and the author are still more talked about than read. "Malthusian" has come to be a common adjective—to be hurled scornfully at people with whom one disagrees, or to be used as a label to indicate the self-evident nature of the danger of over-population. Like so many other adjectives of common controversy, "Malthusian" seems to have a different meaning in the hands of every author. But the wide usage and the very variety of meanings form a tribute to the importance of Malthus and his book.

Malthus made no claims to originality. He regarded himself as a follower of Hume and Adam Smith. The first draft of his *Essay* arose out of discussion with his father about a book by William Godwin, called *The Enquirer.* Godwin, like Rousseau and Condorcet, was a firm believer in the perfectibility of man. He looked forward to the day when each man, doing what seemed right in his own eyes, would also be doing what was, in fact, best for the community, because all would be guided by principles of reason.

The end of the eighteenth century was a period of great hope for the future of man. As Malthus himself wrote:

The great and unlooked for discoveries that have taken place of late years in natural philosophy; the increasing diffusion of general knowledge from the extension of the art of printing; the ardent and unshackled spirit of inquiry that prevails throughout the lettered, and even unlettered world; the new and extraordinary lights that have been thrown on political subjects, which dazzle, and astonish the understanding; and particularly that tremendous phenomenon in the political horizon, the French revolution, which, like a blazing comet, seems destined either to inspire with fresh life and vigour, or to scorch up and destroy the shrinking inhabitants of the earth, have all concurred to lead many able men into the opinion, that we were touching on a period big with the most important changes, changes that would in some measure be decisive of the future fate of mankind.

With these great possibilities before the world, Malthus wrote, that

the advocate for the present order of things is apt to treat the sect of speculative philosophers, either as a set of artful and designing knaves, who preach up ardent benevolence, and draw captivating pictures of a happier state of society, only the better to enable them to destroy the present establishments, and to forward their own deep-laid schemes of ambition; or, as wild and mad-headed enthusiasts, whose silly speculations, and absurd paradoxes, are not worthy the attention of any reasonable man.

On the other hand, Malthus noted that "the advocate for the perfectibility of man, and of society, retorts on the defender of establishments a more than equal contempt. He brands him as the slave of the most miserable, and narrow prejudices; or as the defender of the abuses of civil society, only because he profits by them."

Styles of writing have changed since 1798; but the content seems remarkably familiar.

Malthus, in this controversy, was trying to be a realist, trying to get at the facts. Looking about him, he could see few signs that man had actually started on this road to perfection. Malthus wrote:

A writer may tell me that he thinks man will ultimately become an ostrich. I cannot properly contradict him. But before he can expect to bring any reasonable person over to his opinion, he ought to shew, that the necks of mankind have been gradually elongating; that the lips have grown harder, and more prominent; that the legs and feet are daily altering their shape; and that the hair is beginning to change into stubs of feathers. And till the probability of so wonderful a conversion can be shewn, it is surely lost time and lost eloquence to expatiate on the happiness of man in such a state; to describe his powers, both of running and flying; to paint him in a condition where all narrow luxuries would be contemned; where he would be employed only in collecting the necessaries of life; and where, consequently, each man's share of labour would be light, and his portion of leisure ample.

The attainment of this happy state was, it seemed to Malthus, blocked by the operation of the laws of nature. He made two basic postulates:

"First, That food is necessary to the existence of man.

"Secondly, That the passion between the sexes is necessary, and will remain nearly in its present form."

These, he points out, seem to have been fixed laws of human nature ever since we have had any knowledge of man, and we cannot assume that they will change in the absence of any direct evidence that such change is taking place. Yet, with these laws in operation, how can man attain any happy state of perfection?

The consequence of the passion between the sexes is the multiplication of people. This multiplication tends to occur in what Malthus called a "geometric ratio": that is, the more people there are, the more offspring they will produce. He calculated that, unchecked, human population tended to double about every twenty-five years.

Thus, "the power of population is indefinitely greater than the power of the earth to produce subsistence for man." The means of subsistence, at most, can be increased at an "arithmetic ratio." One can imagine the doubling of food production in twenty-five years by bringing new land into cultivation, or by improving agricultural methods. But this carries with it no implicit potentiality for doubling again in the next twenty-five years. At the most, one could expect that continuing improvements in farming practices, in the selection of more prolific breeds, in the cultivation of new land, would result in an addition to subsistence in the next twenty-five years equivalent to the addition of the first twenty-five years. These constant improvements, then, would result in an arithmetic series like 1, 2, 3, 4, 5 . . . But in the meanwhile, the potential population increase is geometric: 1, 2, 4, 8, 16, 32 . . . which rapidly runs to astronomical numbers.

The population potential is not realized because the limits of food supply impose, automatically, conditions of misery—of starvation and semistarvation and disease—for large numbers of mankind. Or because, if the passion between the sexes does not lead to reproduction, it leads to vice.

The germs of existence contained in this spot of earth, with ample food and ample room to expand in, would fill millions of worlds in the course of a few thousand years. Necessity, that imperious all pervading law of nature, restrains them within the prescribed bounds. The race of plants, and the race of animals shrink under this great restrictive law. And the race of man cannot, by any efforts of reason, escape from it. Among plants and animals its effects are waste of seed, sickness and premature death. Among mankind, misery and vice. The former, misery, is an absolutely necessary consequence of it. Vice is a highly probable consequence, and we therefore see it abundantly prevail; but it ought not, perhaps, to be called an absolutely necessary consequence.

This was a bleak outlook indeed. The criticism, the discussion, the search for flaws in the logic, were intense. When, in 1803, Malthus published the revised and enlarged edition of his *Essay,* he stated his basic propositions in a somewhat modified form:

1. Population is necessarily limited by the means of subsistence.

2. Population invariably increases where the means of subsistence increase, unless prevented by some very powerful and obvious checks.

3. These checks, and the checks which repress the superior power of population, and keep its effects on a level with the means

of subsistence, are all resolvable into moral restraint, vice and misery.

An escape, you will note, has been allowed through "moral restraint"—the delaying of marriage until means are assured of supporting the offspring.

This has aptly been called the "dismal theorem" of Malthus. It has had a great influence on Western thought, both in direct and in devious ways. Perhaps its most important influence has been as the basis for the theory of natural selection, for Darwinian evolution.

Charles Darwin acknowledged the debt in his autobiography:

In October 1838, that is, fifteen months after I had begun my systematic enquiry, I happened to read for amusement "Malthus on Population," and being well prepared to appreciate the struggle for existence which everywhere goes on from long-continued observation of the habits of animals and plants, it at once struck me that under these circumstances favourable variations would tend to be preserved, and unfavourable ones to be destroyed. The result of this would be the formation of new species. Here then I had at last got a theory by which to work. . . .

Alfred Russel Wallace quite independently hit upon the theory of natural selection after reading this *Essay* by Malthus, one of those curious "coincidences" in the history of science. The coincidence is logical enough. The idea of the universal tendency among both plants and animals to reproduce beyond the available means of subsistence, with a consequent struggle for existence among competing individuals within a population, led quite naturally to the idea that those individuals most fit, most apt at getting food, would be most likely to survive. Granted heritable variation among the individuals of a population, the constant selection tending toward constant improvement seemed axiomatic.

The sequence of ideas here is a nice example of the inter-relatedness of things. Malthus, looking primarily at a human and social problem, worked out a series of propositions that led to a major biological theory. The biological theory of natural selection in turn led to the whole series of ideas about human economic and political behavior that fall under such a phrase as "social Darwinism." The interaction between social and biological thought, in this case, has to be called "fruitful," whether one likes the flavor of the fruit or not.

In both biological and social sciences, then, the study of populations and of the means of subsistence have been indissolubly linked by the Malthusian theorem. Malthus stated his laws to cover plants and animals as well as men, and it has often been supposed that we are here dealing with a general order of nature. Perhaps so, but I think conclusions should be drawn with caution because of the nature of man, a product as much of culture as of biological forces.

It is hardly possible to quarrel with the two basic laws as stated in the first edition of the *Essay:* that food is necessary to the existence of man (or other organisms); and that the passion between the sexes is necessary, or at least likely to continue. Whether the conclusion follows, that the check on population must derive directly from the limits of subsistence, is something else. Malthus himself proposed one indirect, or "preventive" check under the label of "moral restraint."

The ultimate limit to the size of the population of any particular kind of organism, surely, is the means of subsistence. But as I look about me, I see few signs of organisms living up to this possible limit—some other kind of "limiting factor" seems to come in long before depletion of the food supply starts to operate. It might be helpful if we tried to think about mechanisms that prevent the organism from reproducing right up to the limits of the food supply. The "vice, misery and moral restraint" of Malthus would be labels for such mechanisms; but not very good labels because they are made of loaded words which distract us from the inquiry.

It seems to me that food supply is the direct limiting factor on population only in rare and catastrophic situations—and that these catastrophic situations, when we examine them, turn out with surprising frequency to involve some direct or indirect form of human activity.

As a collector of insects, I have long been impressed with the trouble one has in finding most kinds. Most insects, like most kinds of animals, are relatively scarce, though their food may be common enough. There is some species of fruit fly, for instance, that lives in almost every kind of fruit, but often you must examine hundreds of fruits before you find a worm. If the fruit flies were living up to their means of subsistence, it ought to be as easy to find the larvae of the flies as to find the particular kinds of fruit in which they live.

Or take butterflies. The caterpillars live on plants. The caterpillars of rare kinds of butterflies may live on very common plants—there seems to be little relation between the abundance of a butterfly and the abundance of the plant on which it feeds. Butterfly caterpillars, in general, are rather hard to find, despite the abundance of their fodder. From the caterpillar point of view, the vegetation of the world is a vast accumulation of fodder, almost all going to waste.

Anyone who has struggled with a garden or orchard and fought off the insect pests may raise his eyebrows at this. I'll admit that the cabbage worms, left to their own devices, often live up to and beyond the limits of the cabbage supply. But here is the catastrophic clause, with human interference: the gardener, in making a bed of cabbages, has created an unusual situation as part of his own special technique for getting food, and a whole series of special situations ensue. He sprays the cabbage with Paris green, which quite effectively limits the caterpillar population before it reaches the limits of the food supply. But the intervention of man with Paris green is no more artificial than his arrangement of the garden in the first place, with a concentration of single kinds of plants in beds and with other plants (weeds) carefully eliminated.

The ecological situation in a garden is, in one sense, "natural" —if the opposite be "supernatural." But it is a very special sort of a situation in which human activity is dominant; and it is hazardous to make comparisons with other situations which have not been altered by man. Man, particularly man with complex culture, seems to upset the "balance of nature." But what is this balance of nature, anyway?

One way of tackling this is to examine the situation of particular kinds of organisms, one after another, to try to determine what actually are the causes of death, the factors that limit the growth of the population. It turns out that we know surprisingly little about the causes of death of animals in nature. It is a very important field of study, but also a very difficult one because it involves keeping close track of large numbers of animals in their actual habitat—meadow, forest or pond. But I know of no instance in which the major cause of death under ordinary circumstances seems to be lack of food, starvation. Other sorts of controlling factors come into operation long before the limits of the food supply are reached.

Mostly, animals seem to be killed off by other animals—that is, they become food for something else before they have had a chance to use up their own food supply. The patterns of who eats whom in the biotic community—grasshoppers eaten by frogs eaten by snakes eaten by hawks—are called "food chains." These generally involve small animals being eaten by somewhat bigger ones; common animals being eaten by less common ones; everything pyramiding on the vegetation that captures the energy of the sun and keeps the whole thing going.

If these relations were all really direct, the system of nature would indeed be in a precarious balance, and the whole thing would be liable to catastrophe from an accident even to some inconspicuous link in one of the chains. Yet, in fact, the system of nature seems to be extraordinarily stable—except where man, with his far-reaching powers, messes it up. It is apparently well supplied with compensating mechanisms that take up slacks and allow for all sorts of shifts in details of numbers. The balance of nature, when we examine it closely, is found to be a teetering affair, with many sorts of regular and irregular fluctuations in animal populations; but in a broad view, these shifts disappear and we get the impression of a fairly steady state.

Man, of course, in one sense is a part of this system of nature —he can't escape it without escaping from the biosphere of our earth. In another sense, however, man has moved out of the system of nature as his more and more elaborate systems of culture have developed. We come again to the question of the relations between organic and cultural evolution. In studying animal populations we are dealing with adaptations that are the product of the long and slow processes of organic evolution; with human populations, the faster tempo of cultural change confronts us at every turn—sometimes with adaptations, and sometimes with behavior (such as war) that hardly seems adapted to the survival of the species.

The cultural factors in population, however, must have been built on biological factors which were gradually replaced or modified during the course of man's Pleistocene development. To get some inkling of population-subsistence relations in evolving man, we have no recourse except to study such relations among existing animal populations, especially the social mammals near the top of the food chain. What limits their populations, if not the availability of food?

We find here a curious mechanism called "territoriality," which has only recently come to be appreciated by biologists. It seems to have many implications in human behavior and evolution.

General recognition of the importance of territory in animal behavior dates from the publication, in 1920, of a book by Eliot Howard, called *Territory in Bird Life*. Howard, as a result of careful observation of the habits of songbirds in his English garden, came to realize that the activities of each nesting pair were largely confined to a limited range of territory, and that the male of the pair actively defended this territory from intrusion, especially by other males of the same species. These territories were "staked out" by the males when they first arrived in the spring, and it appeared that an important function of bird song was the proclamation of territory ownership—providing a warning that this area was already pre-empted.

Mammals, birds, reptiles, and even fish have been found to show territorial behavior. Most commonly, the territory covers the mating, nesting and feeding grounds, but sometimes it includes only the mating and nesting areas, and sometimes the mating area only. The territory may be occupied by single individuals, by pairs or families, or, in social animals, by the herd or flock. Where flocks of birds nest together, the immediate vicinity of each nest may be defended as a territory by the occupants.

The essence of the territorial concept is that the "owners" of territory are always ready to defend it against intruders, particularly of their own kind; and a given individual, on home territory, often shows fearless, aggressive behavior quite different from the behavior shown when off the territory. These relationships result in the spacing of the population of a given species, and it seems that availability of territories may be the actual factor that limits the possible maximum size of the population of a species in a particular place.

When all of the suitable territories for a particular species of mammal have been occupied, the surplus individuals become homeless wanderers, constantly driven on into strange places by their more fortunate, established fellows. Paul Errington has gathered an impressive amount of evidence indicating that it is these homeless individuals that are most often killed by predators; that mice, for instance, on their home territories, are relatively immune from the attacks of owls and hawks. The animals caught by these predators are the wanderers, who have been unable to establish territories.

This territorial concept introduces an important modification of the idea that the numbers of an animal are limited by the food supply. The limitation may, in the long run, hold because the size of the territory defended by any individual or group may depend on the scarcity or abundance of food. But territories often seem to cover more ground than might be needed, so that they may in fact serve to insure that a species does not live up to the limit of possible food supply under normal circumstances.

The monkeys and apes, as far as they have been studied in the field, all show territorial behavior, and I have no doubt that this characterized the primate ancestors of the human stock, and early man as well.

C. R. Carpenter's study of the howler monkeys of Barro Colorado Island in Panama illustrates territorial behavior in a social primate. He found the monkey population of the six-square-mile island to include about 490 individuals, divided into 28 clans. The clans varied in size from a low of four animals to a high of 35 animals, with an average of 18 animals. Generally, there were about three adult males and seven adult females, with associated infants and young, in such a clan.

Each clan was found to range over a definite and restricted territory, which varied in size according to the nature of the forest and the number of monkeys in the clan. Within the territory there were certain trees that were used repeatedly for sleeping, and certain areas that seemed to be preferred feeding grounds. The outward parts of a territory were less frequented than these central foci, and the total territory covered by any particular clan rarely overlapped the territories of neighboring clans. The clans tended to avoid one another, and when two did come together at the margins of their respective territories, there would be a vigorous vocal "battle," the males of the two groups hurling defiance at one another after the howler fashion which, because of their extraordinary vocal equipment, sounds terrifying enough to the human observer.

When we turn from social mammals to men living at a food-gathering stage of culture, we find them everywhere to be organized into small groups of several families—clans—each of which occupies a definite territory. The clan and territorial organization seems quite comparable with that found in the howler monkeys, the baboons and the wolves; and I cannot doubt, then, that it has a very ancient basis in human nature.

Daryll Forde, in describing the conditions of life of the Semang Negritos of the Malay forests, has perhaps pictured conditions that were generally prevalent in the Pleistocene.

Each group, which is usually a large family of parents and grown children with their families, has its small traditional territory of some twenty square miles, over which its claim to the especially valuable fruits of certain trees is recognized among its neighbors. For hunting and collecting of roots it is free to wander over the lands of neighboring groups, but it always returns to gather the heavy green prickly fruit of the tall durian trees in its own territory. Since the group must gather its daily food as it travels, movement is slow, and it does not cover a wide extent of territory: five or six miles would be a fair day's travel. Within any given locality a number of groups are in fairly frequent contact, but beyond a radius of twenty to thirty miles encounters are very rare. Thus there arise small agglomerations of groups which from their frequent contacts maintain a similarity of speech and feel some sense of community, while a few miles away the dialect may change so markedly that intercourse is difficult and we have entered the sphere of another collection of groups. These agglomerations can hardly be spoken of as tribes, for they have no set organization and do not act consciously as a body. Their character and size is a function of the limited mobility of each component group.

The Australian aborigines show a similar group and territory organization. Spencer and Gillen, writing about the Arunta, note that the tribe

is divided into a larger number of small local groups, each of which occupies, and is supposed to possess, a given area of country, the boundaries of which are well known to the natives. . . . Still further examination of each local group reveals the fact that it is composed largely, but not entirely, of individuals who describe themselves by the name of some one animal or plant. . . . The area of country which is occupied by each of these, which will be spoken of as local totemic groups, varies to a considerable extent, but is never very large, the most extensive one with which we are acquainted being that of the witchetty grub people of the Alice Springs district. This group, at the time we first knew it in 1896, was represented by exactly forty individuals (men, women and children) and the area of which they were recognized as the proprietors extended over about 100 square miles.

Clan and territory would thus give an organization for the population, with primitive man as with other social mammals. The maximum possible size of the group would be more or less automatically limited by the nature of the food-gathering ac⌄ tivities. The collection of fruits, roots and small game is prac⌐ tical only for rather small bands; with larger groups, the individuals would soon start getting in each other's way. Larger bands would be advantageous for preying on large herds of grazing animals, but such hunting bands would also require much larger territories.

Exactly how the size of the band and the size of the territory would be determined is not clear—one wishes here that there were many more observations both on primitive men and on territorial mammals. Probably many factors operated. There is evidence way back in the Pleistocene that man was one of the principal enemies of man, and territorial strife may have come into the picture early. It is easy to imagine the threats and squabblings of animals like howler monkeys turning into fatal combat with man, and this will be examined in a later chapter on the effect of war and other forms of homicide on population history.

It is also clear that some form of population limitation, especially infanticide, has been widespread among food-gathering peoples in recent times; and this practice may have an ancient history. It is also easy to imagine the origins of this practice among small bands wandering over definite territories, providing conditions that would make an excess of young children not only a present inconvenience but an obvious future threat to the resources of the group.

Bands must sometimes have split, temporarily or permanently; and individuals must often either have strayed from bands or been ejected from them, as happens now with social mammals. And with man, as with other animals, the lone individual with no settled territory would have been the most likely victim of the hazards of the environment.

We really don't know enough, either about man or other mammals, to be sure how territoriality works in every case: but the result seems clear. As Bartholomew and Birdsell have phrased it in a recent article in the *American Anthropologist,* territoriality

distributes the individual organisms or social units of a species throughout the entire accessible area of suitable habitat. Should the population increase, local population density does not continue to build up indefinitely. Instead, territorial defense forces individuals out into marginal situations, and thus the resources of the optimal habitat are not exhausted. Most of the displaced individuals do not survive, but some may find unexploited areas of suitable habitat and thus extend the range of the species. The result is that a population tends to be maintained at or below the optimum density in the preferred habitat, and the excess individuals are forced into marginal areas to which they must adapt or die.

With the shift from food gathering to food production—with the domestication of animals and plants—the strictly biological pattern of band and territory gave way to new patterns that are more readily understood in cultural terms. Culture must have started its influence on population relations long before, with the accumulation and transmission of knowledge of special ways of hunting and fishing and using wild plants, with the development of varying attitudes toward children and death and outsiders. The history of man's progress in manipulating and exploiting his environment with techniques that were learned and taught must be a long one. But the discovery that food could be grown, that the food production of the environment could be arranged, amounted to a revolution in the relationship between man and his environment, population and the means of subsistence.

It almost looks as though man had escaped from the ordinary laws of nature. He hadn't, of course, because he was still living in the biosphere and still trapped by such things as the laws of energy transfer within that system. But he was clearly involved with a whole new set of environmental relationships, with consequences that are still far from clear.

The change from food gathering to food producing is often called the "Neolithic Revolution." The term "Neolithic" or "New Stone Age" was first applied because of the change from chipping to polishing stone, but it is clear now that all sorts of changes went along with this and that the key change was not implement manufacture, but agriculture. A given tract of fertile ground could now support many more people than before, and they could stay in the same place, coming to form a village. How this first occurred, where, and when are still far from clear. The evidence seems to indicate that it was somewhere on the margin of the tropics in the Old World, perhaps in the valley of the Nile, the Tigris-Euphrates, or the Indus, and perhaps ten thousand years or so ago. We do not know whether the idea of planting crops occurred only once and spread, or whether the discovery was made independently several times and in several different places.

Speculation about the origins of agriculture, as about the origins of any kind of human activity, is a fascinating business. It isn't all speculation, either, because careful detective work by archeologists and by biologists has revealed a great deal of factual information around which the speculation can be oriented. In this book, however, our focus is on the changed population-resources relationships. If, in general, the relations between populations and the means of subsistence must be studied in *ecological* terms, with post-Neolithic man, such studies must be made in *economic* terms. The measure of the difference between man and other organisms is in the meaning of these words—ecology and economics.

It is interesting, in this connection, that Malthus was the first person to have the title of "Professor of Political Economy." He taught this subject at Haileybury, the college that the East India Company set up for the training of its personnel. Economics, in Malthus' day, was a young science, and the word ecology hadn't yet been invented. Yet now we have these two great fields of knowledge which hedge about and modify the misleading—but challenging—simplicity of the Malthusian propositions.

The complexity of human economy seems not to have been a steady growth, but rather a matter of spurts, and at least two other "revolutions" equivalent to that of the Neolithic can be recognized—the Urban Revolution and the Industrial Revolution. The urban revolution, which involved the development of specialization of labor, storage and transportation of food, and the other technical and social changes that make the city possible, again revolutionized the relation between man and his means of subsistence. The beginning of cities marks the beginning of what we call civilization, with all of the connotations that have gathered around that word. The numbers of people multiplied enormously, and the unit of population organization moved from the band to the village and tribe to the city and empire. Single organizations, like those of Persia, China and Rome, might include at one time more people than had existed in the whole world under a pre-Neolithic economy.

The industrial revolution, which turned chiefly perhaps on the harnessing of power other than that of slaves and beasts, again changed completely the relations between man and his resources. We are perhaps too near this revolution to understand completely its implications in population terms, though we can see vividly enough the first effects in the change from a world population of half a billion in 1650 to two and a half billion in 1950. Much of this spurt has been due to the use of capital resources—of the fossil fuels of coal and oil—and alarm about the future has been based on the fact that these are clearly limited in supply. Perhaps the physicists have found a way out with their tapping of the energy of the atomic nucleus; perhaps other ways will be found. Very likely we shall have other revolutions—but a revolution, almost by definition, is not predictable.

However, man's biological nature has carried right on through these revolutions in economy. Birth and death remain basically biological phenomena, however much their incidence may be affected by the economic factors. Their incidence certainly has been affected by these economic—cultural—changes. Perhaps the best way of getting at that is to go back and look at particular factors governing birth rates and death rates, trying to tease out the biological and cultural elements that enter into changes in these rates.

CHAPTER *6* HUMAN REPRODUCTION

The human population of the globe at any given time is the result of the number of individuals previously added to it (reproduction) less those removed from it (mortality). To understand the population situation of a given place or region, we must also take into account the movement of people—migration into or out of the region. These three words, reproduction, mortality, and migration, thus provide us with labels for basic subdivisions of population study and a frame for the next several chapters of this book.

Reproduction involves sex. There is, of course, the amoeba that splits in two from time to time, thus making more amoebas. And virgin birth is quite common among plant lice and some kinds of wasps, but the biologist views this parthenogenesis as a special manifestation of sex, rather than as a variety of sexless reproduction. Sex is almost, if not quite, universal. Throughout the diverse orders, classes and phyla of the plant and animal

80

kingdoms, reproduction regularly, periodically, or occasionally, involves some sort of a sexual process—that is, the new individual is the product not of a single antecedent individual, but of a fusion of materials from two antecedent individuals, from two parents.

This fusion arrangement, sexual reproduction, is so universal that it must have a profound significance. There is evidence that it occurs in the most simple kinds of life, in protozoa, bacteria and viruses, though the routine, day-to-day method of multiplication with such organisms is usually some asexual process of splitting or budding. With the more complex organisms, such as flowering plants and vertebrates, sexual reproduction is universal. With vertebrates, it is the only kind of reproduction known to occur in nature.

The fusion arrangement means that life, in its multiplication, is not endlessly divergent. It means that the guiding stuff of heredity, the germ plasm, forms a pool which can be shared by all members of an interbreeding population, of a species. The unit of evolution, then, is not the individual, but the interbreeding population, the shared pool of hereditary materials.

The study of sex can become very complicated—not only with man, but with almost any animal or plant. There are, in the first place, all of the various factors that govern the production of special sex cells, of spermatozoa and ova in the case of vertebrates and other complex animals. The study of these can involve such wide areas of sciences as physiology, anatomy, cytology and genetics. Then there are the factors that govern the processes whereby sperm from one individual are brought in contact with ova from another individual. There are all sorts of mechanisms for this among the various groups of animals and plants whereby internal events within the organism are coordinated with external events, with the behavior of the organism in its living environment. Finally, there are the factors that govern the development of the new individual formed by the fusion of the sex cells—factors whose study is the province of the special science of embryology.

Students of population, in discussing human reproduction, distinguish between *fecundity* and *fertility*. Fecundity refers to the capacity of the species to reproduce; fertility to the actual reproductive performance. Fecundity, then, is a sort of ideal maximum, probably never actually attained by man, or perhaps by any other organism. It is the potential reproductive rate, useful for comparing one sort of animal with another, and useful as a sort of standard with which the fertility, actual reproductive performance, can be compared. The study of fecundity, then, is largely physiological—a matter of estimating egg production, sperm production, factors surrounding fertilization, and factors governing embryonic development and birth.

The distinction is firmly entrenched in sociological literature, but it has not been universally taken up by biologists, who are apt to use fertility to mean either the potential or the actual reproductive rate of an organism. It took me a long time to learn to keep the two words straight, and I am still not sure that there is any use in trying to give precise meanings to words that, in the common language, are roughly synonymous. In discussing reproduction, however, it is perhaps logical to start with fecundity, or physiology, and then proceed to fertility, which is probably more a matter of behavior than of physiology (if the two are separable).

The physiology of the female limits possible human fecundity. The reproductive life of the individual covers some thirty-five years between puberty (menarche) and menopause. During this period an ovum may become ripe approximately every 28 days. If the ovum is fertilized, ovulation is suspended during the ensuing nine months during which the embryo is developing; and if the infant is breast-fed, ovulation may be very irregular for some time after birth. The average human female thus has a potentiality of producing something like 20 offspring, without allowance for twin births.

Very large families by one mother generally include twins. Thus the world's record seems to be held by an Austrian woman, Mrs. Bernard Scheinberg, who bore sixty-nine children—quadruplets four times, triplets seven times, and twins sixteen times. It is usually calculated that twins, among Europeans, occur once in 85 confinements, triplets once in 7,629 confinements, and quadruplets once in 670,734.

The factors governing multiple births in man are not well understood. There are, of course, two kinds of twins—identical twins that come from the same fertilized egg which splits in half at a very early stage in growth to form two individuals; and fraternal twins, which result when two ova ripen at the same time. The identical twins thus have exactly the same heredity from both parents, which makes them of great interest to geneticists trying to untangle hereditary and environmental influence in man. The fraternal twins are no more alike than any other siblings (brothers or sisters) except that they are of the same age.

There seems to be some hereditary basis for twinning, because it frequently runs in families, even though not to the extreme represented by Mrs. Scheinberg. The tendency toward twinning—either identical or fraternal—may be transmitted by either parent. In the case of identical twins, the mechanism would seem to be some property of the fertilized egg that tended to cause it to split apart. In the case of fraternal twins, the maternal element seems easy enough to understand—the tendency to ripen more than one ovum at a given ovulation. There is also evidence, however, that when two eggs are present, certain fathers have more than average probability of siring twins—perhaps because of unusually active and vigorous sperm.

The twinning rate varies among different peoples. Among

the Chinese and Japanese, for instance, twinning is only about half as frequent as among Europeans; and among American Negroes it is more frequent (about one twin in 70 births) than among the paleface element in the population. There may have been a certain amount of selection against twinning during human evolution, because most contemporary primitive peoples view twins as something abnormal and evil, and one or both are destroyed at birth. A few peoples view twins as a favorable omen, a sign of conception by some beneficent spirit; and in such societies twins are brought up with care. Under the food-gathering economy of the Pleistocene, however, twins must have been a real handicap to the mother and the social group, so that practical considerations would reinforce superstition and lead to their destruction.

An important element in human fecundity is the length of the reproductive life of the female. This is taken to begin with puberty—a complex process involving many changes in the structure and functioning of the body. One of these changes, the onset of menstruation, is generally taken to be a sort of index to the whole process; and figures on "age at puberty" in a given population thus mean "age at first menstruation." This is fairly easily determined datum, and many studies on the subject have been made in various parts of the world—but with curiously conflicting results. Some authors have shown that puberty is earlier in one race than another; and others have come out with precisely contrary results.

It looks as though age at puberty were determined by several different factors. There is probably a genetic element—some individuals having an inherent tendency to mature earlier than others. Fairly surely there is a nutritional element, for puberty tends to occur earlier in better nourished populations. The amount and kind of exercise may also be influential. In the United States, age at first menstruation is now lower than it was two or three generations ago, which may be due to improved nutrition. There may also be climatic and racial differences, but these seem generally to be swamped by the nutritional factor.

The average age at first menstruation in the United States now is somewhere between 13½ and 14 years. Among the Jivaro Indians of South America, the first menstruation is said to occur at about the age of ten, which is the lowest figure I have come across. More generally, for diverse peoples, the average age is said to be 14, or 15, or 16.

It seems very likely that fertility remains low for several years after this first menstruation, though definite statistics on this are not available. In a great many societies there is a fairly complete sexual freedom among the adolescents; yet births outside of the marital relationship are relatively rare. Contraception, abortion, infanticide, or enforced marriage certainly occur in such societies; but it is hard to believe that these would be frequent enough to account for the surprising infrequency of childbearing by adolescent girls. As Clellan Ford observes:

it seems likely that, in addition to these social factors, the first few years after the menses appear is a period of relative sterility. A considerable amount of data in substantiation of this possibility have been collected by physiologists and anthropologists. The explanation for this period of relative sterility is not known, but it is believed that fecundity depends upon a general physical maturation process which is incomplete at menarche.

Each of the two ovaries, at maturity, contains about 30,000 eggs—the total life supply, but a more than adequate one. One of these eggs "ripens" during each menstrual cycle and passes into the oviduct, or Fallopian tube, where fertilization, if it occurs, takes place. It is thought that the egg remains available for fertilization for about 24 hours, and that spermatozoa in the oviduct remain viable for about 48 hours, so successful fertilization involves rather close timing. The whole idea of birth control through abstinence from intercourse except during "safe periods" depends on this; and a considerable amount of study has centered on the determination of the precise time of ovulation.

Unfortunately, from the birth control point of view, ovulation cannot be predicted with precision. It occurs about halfway between menstruations—some authors fixing it rather precisely at 15 days before the onset of menstruation—but the menstrual cycle itself is variable, from individual to individual and from time to time. The range, in general, is between 21 and 34 days.

Physiologists have exercised a deal of ingenuity in trying to find a precise test for the occurrence of ovulation, and various methods have been worked out. It has become apparent, from this work, that ovulation does not occur during every menstrual cycle—that both in monkeys and in men, there may be "anovulatory" cycles. Further study of the conditions governing this irregularity of ovulation may shed light on various problems of human fertility.

Menstruation, and ovulation, become increasingly irregular with age, and finally cease with the menopause, usually somewhere between the ages of 45 and 50. I haven't found any statistics on possible differences in age at menopause among different people. It is a much less definite phenomenon than menarche, with symptoms spread over a period of three to five years.

Of the numerous changes involved in male puberty, the significant element from the point of view of reproduction is the appearance of an ejaculate with motile sperm. Figures on the timing of this are not easy to come by. Kinsey, in his study of American males, found the average age at first ejaculation to be 13.9 years, and that in 90 per cent of the population it first occurred somewhere between the ages of 11 and 15. He found a significant difference among educational classes (which he used as a convenient way of determining social level); the mean age for first ejaculation was 14.6 years for boys who never go beyond grade school, 14.0 for boys not going beyond high school, and 13.7 for boys going to college. This difference, as he points out, probably reflects the better nutrition of boys who have higher educational facilities open to them. It thus seems that nutrition is an important factor in determining the timing of sexual maturity in both males and females.

A boy may be able to achieve ejaculation at the age of 14, but this does not necessarily prove that he is physiologically capable of fatherhood—the little understood phenomenon of adolescent sterility again enters in. The presence of motile sperm is far from proving that an individual is fecund, as has been nicely shown by the careful studies of Edmond Farris on male sterility among married couples. Only a single sperm is needed for the fertilization of a single ovum, but apparently a very large number of sperm must be released in the female to make sure that one finds its way to the egg in the oviduct.

Farris found that a highly fertile male is one who averages more than 185 million moving spermatozoa in the total ejaculate; that a relatively infertile male is one with fewer than 80 million. Farris avoids using the word "sterile" when any moving sperm are present in the ejaculate. Individuals differ greatly in the volume of total ejaculate (from 1 to 10 cc.), in the number of spermatozoa per cc. of ejaculate, and in the percentage of defective spermatozoa. These all also vary in one individual, depending on the frequency of coitus. There may commonly be 500 million or more spermatozoa in a total ejaculate. I have not come across any studies of variation in a single individual with age, or with diet or other environmental factors, but such variations surely occur. The volume of ejaculate and total number of sperm is largest after a period of five days or so of sexual abstinence; so that frequency of coitus may have a direct bearing on male fertility, especially with males in the "subfertile" category.

The reproductive life does not end as sharply in the human male as in the human female, and there are numerous instances of males at quite advanced ages fathering children. There are, nevertheless, age changes that roughly parallel those of the female; and as Kinsey has shown so nicely with his statistics, there is a steady and continuous decline in sexual activity on the part of the male as he grows older.

When we put male physiology and female physiology together, and try to work out the physiology of conception, conception seems a most improbable event. The egg is available for fertilization only for a brief period, perhaps 24 hours; the sperm in their millions are released in the vagina, and must travel some seven or eight inches to the point where the egg rests in the oviduct—an immense distance for a microscopic sperm that travels, at the very best, three millimeters a minute. A single-minded and persistent sperm could, in theory, make the trip in something like an hour; but since much of the sperm movement is probably random, it may be several hours before the first one reaches its goal. When we sum up all of the hazards of egg development and sperm development, and add the improbability of a properly timed rendezvous, the odds against conception seem immense. Yet it occurs all the time—as witnessed by the birth statistics of the human species.

Generally among animals, the female is sexually receptive only at the time of ovulation; and there are complex physiological and behavioral mechanisms to insure that copulation will occur at that time. Psychologists have long tried to find traces of this periodicity in man, especially of periodicity of sexual desire on the part of the female, but they have been unable to find any very clear or convincing evidence. The great apes and other primates all show changes in female behavior at ovulation, which tend to insure copulation at that time, and similar behavior must once have characterized the human stock. But periodicity in sexual interest seems to have dropped out somewhere in the

Pleistocene, leaving the proper timing of copulation a purely chance affair. Without such physiological guidance, man becomes preoccupied with sex practically all of the time—which has its advantages as well as its disadvantages.

The frequency of sexual intercourse may, then, have an important bearing on fecundity, since proper timing is so largely a matter of chance. The more frequent intercourse, the more likely that sperm will be on hand at the right time. There may be a joker in this—the observation by Farris that frequent intercourse results in a lowering of male fecundity. Farris was primarily interested in sterility in married couples in the United States, and consequently many of his subjects were "subfertile" males. His "highly fertile" males could produce high sperm counts even with frequent ejaculations. There is no way of knowing what proportion of males in a general population would belong to these different fertility groups.

Several studies have been made of the frequency of sexual intercourse among married couples in the United States. As might be expected, it turns out that there is a very great variation in habit, from couples who have intercourse one or more times a day, on the average, to those who may average only once a month, or less. There are differences among various social and cultural groups, and great differences with age. Kinsey, whose statistics are based on the largest sample, found the average frequency of marital intercourse to drop from 3.9 per week at age 20, to 2.9 at age 30, to 1.8 at age 50, and to 0.9 at age 60.

Contraception is so widespread in the United States that it is difficult to make any study of the relation between frequency of intercourse and fecundity. Raymond Pearl was able to carry out a study of the relation between coitus and reproduction in 199 married couples in Baltimore—apparently normal and healthy people who practised no form of contraception. He found, on an average, 351 copulations associated with each pregnancy. "If only potentially effective copulations be considered, there were, on the average, 254 for each pregnancy. In other words, 253 out of each 254 copulations, on the average, that conceivably might have been effective were actually without reproductive result even though no attempt at contraception was made." Pearl did not break down his data to show whether couples who copulated more frequently had, on the average, more children.

In other societies, very little seems to be known about frequency of intercourse within the marital relationship, although there is a great deal of information in the anthropological literature on the circumstances under which intercourse is tabooed. Of these taboos, that on intercourse during menstruation is most widespread. This, however, would have no effect on fecundity, since conception is rare at that time. Customs which would tend to favor intercourse at the time of ovulation seem not to have been described; and various cultures have, in fact, quite erroneous ideas about the circumstances of coitus most favorable for conception.

The belief has sometimes been expressed that primitive peoples, as compared with the civilized, are "undersexed," that they require the stimulation of dances, feasts or other special stimulation for sexual activity. And then, of course, there is the contrary belief, that sex occupies a more prominent place in savage than in civilized life.

The Western European culture to which we belong has gone to particular lengths to channel and restrict sexual behavior; yet it seems not to have been particularly successful in either the channeling or the restriction. One might guess that there is probably more preoccupation with sex, more time and energy spent in sexual activity, in this Western culture than in most others. Where other cultures seem more active sexually, it may be that this activity is simply more overt, less clandestine. One is given pause by the statistics dredged up by the Kinsey study that "only 45.9 per cent of the total outlet of the total population is derived from marital intercourse." This figure is based on males, and I suspect that these are more addicted to masturbation, the patronage of prostitutes, homosexuality, and such like nonreproductive sexual outlets than are the females. But even with American females, there is surely a great deal of sexual behavior that can hardly be called "reproductive."

Sexual behavior, with all known peoples, is under strong social or cultural controls, so that it is very difficult if not impossible to arrive at any clear idea of what is "natural" or "normal" for animal man. The study of sexual behavior in man thus becomes more involved with culture than with physiology— though the cultural proliferations must all have their roots in some physiological or psychological process. The search for the beginnings of human sexual diversity in the behavior of monkeys and apes may thus be helpful in understanding man's animal baseline. But with man sex has, to an extraordinary degree, become divorced from reproduction and become an end in itself. If the psychologists who look for sexual sublimations or origins in man's creative activities are correct, this freeing of sex, which has made reproduction an almost incidental and accidental consequence, may be directly and indirectly responsible for a good share of the qualities that we hold dear in ourselves. It has also undoubtedly had a lot of consequences that seem less clearly fortunate.

Which goes to show how easy it is, when writing about sex, to get away from the subject of reproduction, our real concern in the present chapter.

Human reproduction is most commonly stated in terms of number of births per year per thousand of population. This is called the "crude birth rate" and it is crude because it fails to take into account the number of females of reproductive age present in the population—a number that may vary greatly from region to region, or from one period of time to another. These "age adjusted" birth rates have a limited usefulness, however, because the necessary data are difficult to come by. It is hard enough to get the data necessary for calculating crude birth rates in past times and in regions where careful censuses have not been made.

The highest reproductive rates known for man are about 50 births per thousand population per year. The figure for the United States in 1800, when the population was going through as rapid an expansion as any ever observed, has been calculated at 55 per thousand. Similar rates have been recorded for the Ukraine in 1866-70 (48.9 per thousand); a careful study in Bengal in India in 1921 gave a rate of 46.7 per thousand; and in a Chinese community in 1931-35, a rate of 45.1 per thousand.

The places that probably have the highest birth rates at the present time also have the poorest statistics, so that little faith can be put in the official figures. The highest reported rates are for countries like Egypt, Chile and Guatemala, all around 40 per thousand so that no doubt such rates also persist in other essentially agricultural countries. Warren Thompson has estimated that 60 per cent of the world's population today may have birth rates of between 40 and 50 per thousand.

In Europe and North America the birth rates have fallen sharply during the last century. In the United States, the rate has fallen from 38 per thousand in 1860, to 30 per thousand in 1900, to 17 per thousand in 1940. In France the decline started earlier, and the birth rate in 1840 was only 28 per thousand, falling to 15 per thousand in 1940. Similar trends have been shown by all of the countries of Western Europe; the decline set in later in Italy, Spain and Portugal, but the trend is equally clear.

The birth rate started to rise again in the United States and some other countries about 1940, and this rise has been especially characteristic of the postwar years. There has been a great deal of discussion among demographers about the meaning of this. It is clearly associated with the war boom and postwar prosperity in the United States; and for a while it was thought to represent births that had been "postponed" from the depression years. People certainly are marrying earlier than a generation ago and having children more frequently. But there seems no likelihood that the trend toward controlled families, "planned parenthood," will be reversed.

The declining birth rate of the West, beyond any doubt, is a cultural, not a physiological phenomenon, and reflects the spread of contraception through our civilization. But this subject, the control of reproduction, warrants treatment in a chapter by itself.

CHAPTER **7** THE CONTROL OF REPRODUCTION

We are apt to think of birth control as a new thing—something characteristic of modern Europe and America, a response to the greatly reduced hazards of life brought about by modern medicine, and to the changed value systems of modern, industrialized society. The phrase "birth control" is certainly modern, and overt and organized propaganda about the need for the restriction of conceptions is also modern—stemming from the impact of Malthus' *Essay* on social thinkers. But the conscious control of reproduction, by individuals, families or societies, appears to be an ancient and widespread human trait. My object in this present chapter is to look at the subject from this general historical and cultural point of view, in the hope of giving some perspective to the contemporary situation.

The elegant word for birth control is *contraception,* the prevention of conception or fertilization. This, clearly, is only one of several ways in which the reproduction of the population might deliberately be slowed or controlled. Reproduction may

94

be restricted by restriction of sexual intercouse itself—and restrictions of one sort or another on sexual intercourse seem to be a universal of human culture. Or, sexual intercourse being allowed, steps may be taken to control conception—birth control or contraception in the strict sense. Or, conception having occurred, the development of the embryo may be stopped—abortion. Or, birth having occurred and the new infant being unwanted by the mother, the family or the society, it may be destroyed—infanticide.

None of these implies any sophisticated realization of the ultimate end—population control. The motivation, in fact, has probably generally been an immediate and family affair, turning on whether more children would be an advantage or an increased nuisance. The Australian blackfellow, using infanticide, is thus not too different from the modern American, using a contraceptive device. There are a few exceptions, in which control of reproduction seems to derive from an awareness by the society as a whole of the necessity of limiting its numbers because of the limitations of available general resources. Some of the Polynesian societies, confined to the resources of small islands, seem to have had this social concept.

There are no known human societies in which there are not some cultural restrictions on sexual intercourse, at least in the form of some sort of incest taboo. This universality of incest prohibitions of one sort or another has long presented a challenge to scholars seeking explanations of human behavior, and the writings on the subject by anthropologists and psychologists are voluminous. Fortunately for me, there seems to be no need to summarize the various theories here.

The universality of incest restrictions is related to the universality of some sort of a marriage arrangement, of some sort of a family system sanctioned by the society. The marriage or family system probably serves primarily to systematize responsibility for the raising of children, but it also tends in some degree to systematize sexual activities. Almost all known human societies recognize the relation between sexual activities and reproduction. I have to say "almost" on account of the Australian aborigines who are so often alleged not to recognize the relationship. The obtuseness of the Australians in this regard may be exaggerated.

Spencer and Gillen, in their very careful study of one Australian tribe, the Arunta, say that "the idea is firmly held that the child is not the direct result of intercourse, that it may come without this, which merely, as it were, prepares the mother for the reception and subsequent birth of a child who, in spirit form, inhabits one of the local totem centres." But if intercourse is thought to prepare the way for the child, this surely represents a recognition of a relationship between copulation and pregnancy. After all, the clarification of the precise relationship between male and female elements in fertilization is an achievement of modern science, and diverse peoples have held very different beliefs on the subject—including beliefs in circumstances under which pregnancy could occur without copulation.

The question of the origin of marriage and the diversity of marital customs among known peoples forms a fascinating subject for investigation, well worked by many scholars, but rather outside our present line of inquiry. The various systems serve to channel the direction of sexual activity, but they usually also enable every female of reproductive age to function sexually and, to a lesser extent, leave some form of sexual outlet open to reproductive males. This sort of generalization breaks down most strikingly among civilized peoples, where spinsterhood may be so common as to affect reproductive rates.

Sex is thus always subject to some sort of social regulation. In general, sex and food are the subjects most commonly surrounded by regulating taboos in human societies. Who eats with whom and under what circumstances is almost as often subject

to social control as who sleeps with whom. Sex taboos have persisted more strongly into our own culture than food taboos;
so that sex seems to be of overwhelming importance in the
psychology of the West. But, as Audrey Richards has pointed
out, cultures can be found where the reverse is true, and where
psychological study might well turn up food preoccupations in
the subconscious as often as such study turns up sex with us.
Even with us, men in a camp restricted to a limited and mo-
notonous diet will talk about strawberries, beefsteaks and oysters
as frequently as they talk about blondes. Press the food restriction further, and a whole apparatus of black market will develop,
like a system of prostitution.

I suppose the analogy could be developed in a variety of ways.
There is even a faint similarity between sexual perversions and
food perversions. At least anthropologists tell us that in the
matter of sex, what is regarded as perverse in one culture may be
regarded as ordinary in another—which would make repugnance to a particular sexual activity comparable with repugnance
to a particular food habit, like eating worms. And if we define
sexual perversion as deviation from behavior leading to the
functional goal of reproduction, we could define food perversion
as a deviation from behavior leading to the functional goal of
nutrition, and no doubt find plenty of examples. The Roman
custom of sensual eating followed by an emetic comes to mind
as one sort of case. And it might be interesting to compare the
glutton with the libertine—though at the other extreme, with
chastity and starvation, we get into trouble. We have voluntary
and involuntary fasting—and chastity—but we don't get involuntary epidemic chastity comparable with the famines of history.

But our present interest is in sex, not food. Most of the sex
taboos are probably inconsequential so far as effect on reproduction rate is concerned. Abstinence may be required in relation to
hunting, fishing or farming; or intercourse may be required,

especially in connection with various sorts of rites to insure fertility for crops. Quite commonly, sexual abstinence is required of men before and during a war expedition, and sometimes for a period after return. Abstinence may be required while engaged in certain activities, such as smelting iron or making arrows.

From the point of view of population effect, the most interesting taboos are those on sexual intercourse after childbirth. Taboos of this sort are quite common among a wide variety of people, and the taboo sometimes extends through the whole period while the mother is nursing a child—two or three years. There is considerable evidence that this custom existed among many tribes of American Indians, and it seems to have been quite general in Africa—though it is the sort of custom that breaks down rapidly on contact with "civilized" people. Of the African Bantu, Miss Richards says "sexual intercourse between the parents is definitely tabooed during the first two years after the birth of the child. This taboo appears to be kept with a rather remarkable stringency throughout the Zula-Xosa peoples." As she goes on to remark, "the problem has obvious practical bearings for those missionaries and others who insist on strict monogamy among these tribes."

Anthropologists have almost universally remarked upon the small size of families among nonliterate peoples, and have noted that the children of a given mother were generally spaced several years apart. The taboo on intercourse during lactation may be an important cause of such child-spacing, especially taken in connection with the irregular ovulation of the nursing mother. Other important factors may be contraception, abortion and infanticide.

The evidence for effective contraception among non-Western peoples is slight, and mostly involves *coitus interruptus,* or male withdrawal before ejaculation. Various peoples have an amazing variety of beliefs about contraception, particularly the use of various sorts of herbs and concoctions to reduce fertility, but most of these beliefs are classed as "superstitions." As science has progressed, many primitive superstitions have been found to have some basis in fact; and it is always possible that some of these primitive contraceptive practices have some real effect; but the subject, like that of primitive medicine in general, has hardly been sufficiently studied.

It is, for one thing, very hard to get the "real facts," particularly in relation to materials that are in some way sacred, or that the natives feel may offend the sensibility of the investigator. This is, of course, a difficulty that surrounds the whole subject of sexual practices among diverse peoples—primitive or civilized. The investigator can rarely know the culture he is investigating as intimately as, say, Mr. Kinsey knows ours, and can thus rarely establish a complete rapport with informants, or evaluate the nuances of alleged practices, or determine the fine but important distinction between what is actually done and what the society feels ought to be done. This is an exasperating difficulty, and much of anthropological training is directed toward overcoming it. But it still remains as an obscuring haze over each man's knowledge of any other man.

Many demographers are convinced that interrupted coitus has been—and is—a widespread method of birth control in modern Europe, and that it explains the decline in birth rate that preceded the spread of other contraceptive practices. There is also evidence of its occurrence in more primitive societies. Raymond Firth, in his careful study of a Polynesian society, the Tikopia, found the practice to be a basic trait of the culture. His remarks on this are worth quoting:

The most definite evidence for the reality of the belief of the Tikopia in physiological paternity is their habit of controlling conception by restraint on the part of the male. In people of this cultural status it is surprising to find such a well-developed technique for dealing with the problem of fertility, and I made frequent enquiries on the subject for some time before accepting the first statements I received. The method of contraception adopted is *coitus interruptus*. It is practiced for two reasons: by married people who do not desire to enlarge their family, and by young men who do not wish to make a girl pregnant and so be forced to marry. The love life of the young people is termed "the casual strolling of the unmarried."

Just as the principal motive of a young man in such cases is to avoid marriage and its responsibilities, so that of a married pair is the avoidance of the extra economic liability which a child brings. In this small but flourishing community there is conscious recognition of the need for correlating the size of population with that of the available land. Consequently it is from this point of view that limitation of families is mainly practiced. The position is expressed very clearly by the people themselves. Here is a typical statement: "Families by Tikopia custom are made corresponding to orchards in the woods. If children are produced in plenty, then they go and steal because their orchards are few. So families in our land are not made large in truth; they are made small. If the family groups are large and they go and steal, they eat from the orchards, and if this goes on they kill each other."

And then there is the famous reference to interrupted coitus in the Bible. The King James version (Genesis 38: 7-10) reads:

7. And Er, Judah's firstborn, was wicked in the sight of the Lord; and the Lord slew him. 8. And Judah said unto Onan, Go in unto thy brother's wife, and marry her, and raise up seed to thy brother. 9. And Onan knew that the seed should not be his; and it came to pass, when he went in unto his brother's wife, that he spilled it on the ground, lest that he should give seed to his brother. 10. And the thing which he did displeased the Lord: wherefore he slew him also.

This sin of Onan's has given rise to a great deal of discussion. Somehow "Onanism" has got twisted in some quarters into a synonym for masturbation; and in other quarters the Lord's punishment of Onan is taken as proof that interrupted coitus or any other interference with the "natural" sex process is a mortal sin. In the context, it seems quite clear that the sin of Onan was not so much the spilling of his seed on the ground, as his refusal to meet his obligation to his brother's wife. This obligation to a widowed sister-in-law, called the "levirate" by anthropologists, has existed among many cultures, including the ancient Jews.

Man's attempts to improve on his anatomy frequently include some sort of tampering with the sexual organs, such as circumcision of the male. Such operations generally have no effect on fertility except very indirectly insofar as they are tied up with the general rituals and restrictions involved in coming of age. Castration, of course, would be a very effective means of fertility control; but this particular mutilation is pretty much limited to civilized societies, and to a numerically insignificant number of males used for some special service like guarding royal wives.

There is one possible exception to this general rule about the irrelevance of genital mutilation to fertility. This is the curious practice of subincision, widespread among the aboriginal Australians. Norman Himes, in his *Medical History of Contraception* remarks:

The exact nature of the operation varies in different groups. The urethra may be split open for its entire length from the glans to the scrotum. In other instances the length of the incision varies with the operator. Portions only of the urethra may be dissected out. During ejaculation the semen then dribbles over the testicles. The men have to urinate with widely separated legs. Among the natives the rite is widely distributed geographically throughout Australia. It is a sort of extension of the circumcision rite, and all young males in the tribes employing the rite are operated on before marriage.

Such an operation certainly sounds as though it ought to reduce conceptions, but there is no direct evidence of any such effect. The Australian blackfellows seem to be as fertile as any other food-gathering people, and tribes that practice subincision have maintained their numbers, and even resort to infanticide.

The most effective and widespread methods of population control among preliterate peoples seem to be infanticide and abortion. The horror of infanticide is so firmly rooted in our own culture that it is difficult to realize how exceptional our attitude is. Yet the evidence, combed by Carr-Saunders and other students from the vast storehouse of anthropological observation, is overwhelming. This is less startling when we remember the practices of the Mediterranean civilizations, especially the Greek city-states, that we all read about in our history books.

This can easily get us into the philosophical question of the relativity of morals. The social scientist, making studies of how people behave, what they do, has no business mixing up moral judgments with his observations. Acting as an observing scientist, his chief concern is to get the facts straight—an almost impossible assignment in itself. But the moral issue is not irrelevant. It belongs in another context, in the way we interpret and use the data. The danger lies in assuming that because everyone does it, or most people do it, or a lot of people do it, "it" (whatever it may be) must be all right. War can be—and often is—justified by such a line of reasoning, usually with the accompanying assumption that the mere fact that a practice is widespread must mean that it is derived from some basic and unalterable element of "human nature."

This is a dismal conclusion that seems to me in no way justified. In fact, the salient thing that emerges from cross-cultural study is the plasticity of human nature, which shows that we need not be forever chained by even the most widespread of human practices—such as war. We can, by looking at other ways of life, gain insight into our own; but moral judgment about our own ways must be made in terms of our own values, objectives and purposes. These are beyond the province of any special science.

Moral relativity does have a certain utility in helping us to look at other ways of life, if not in helping us to solve our own problems. In this matter of infanticide, for instance, we can at least observe and describe the practice in terms of the values and purposes of the society in which it occurs. When, by force or persuasion, we are able to modify the moral ideas of other peoples so that they conform more closely with our own, we should at least try to understand the functioning of the institutions that we are changing, and when these functions seem important, find morally acceptable substitutes for the practices that we condemn. Thus there is, in a good part of the Western world, no moral repugnance to contraception, and we would surely generally regard contraception as a moral gain over infanticide; in suppressing the one, then, should we not try to facilitate the other?

Raymond Firth, in his study of the Tikopia, has stated the problem frankly:

The really regrettable feature of the situation is that but for the moral preconceptions of the interpreters of the Christian religion the old checks would act in a perfectly satisfactory manner. A celibacy in which chastity was not enforced, and a discreet infanticide, would serve to maintain the population in equilibrium, and would be in accord with the feeling of the people themselves. An appeal was actually made to me by one of the leading men of Tikopia that on my return to Tulagi I should persuade the Government to pass a law enjoining infanticide after a married pair had had four or five children, in order that the food supply might not be overburdened. I pointed out to him that Europeans have an unconquerable repugnance to the taking of human life, even when it has not really begun to participate in the community, and declined to press the Government in this matter. But I felt then, as I do now, the injustice of enforcing our European moral attitudes

on a people who before our arrival had worked out a satisfactory
adjustment to the population problem—particularly when we can
offer them no adequate solution to the maladjustment which we
thus create.

There is no way, from the literature, of gaining any quantita-
tive measure of the extent of either infanticide or abortion now
or in past times. One would expect abortion to replace infanticide
as societies become more sophisticated, but there seems to be
no clear pattern, and in many instances both practices are reported as occurring in a given society. Infanticide has certainly
persisted into quite sophisticated civilizations, and contrariwise,
relatively unsophisticated peoples may be quite skillful in induc-
ing abortions.

The general prevalence of infanticide and abortion among
contemporary peoples of food-gathering or gardening culture
might be taken as an indication that such forms of population
control were of great antiquity. There is no direct evidence for
Pleistocene man; and the fact that food-gathering peoples today
have a given custom is no proof that men in the Old Stone Age
had comparable customs. When traces of a given behavior pattern can be found in contemporary men and in various sorts of
living primates, the argument for the antiquity of the pattern
is much stronger; but I know of no evidence of infanticide (let
alone abortion) in subhuman primates, nor in any other animals
except under very unusual conditions. How far back in time such
methods of reproductive control extend is, then, purely a matter
of speculation. Certainly a new infant every year would have
been an intolerable nuisance to the female living in the Old
Stone Age, unless a high proportion of the infants died very
early. Perhaps fertility was lower under those conditions, and
perhaps conception was very rare during the prolonged period
when the mother was nursing. Maybe the possibility of conception by a lactating female is, geologically, a recently acquired

human trait which, as it appeared, was offset by the destruction of the intruding infant, or the taboo on intercourse during lactation.

Whatever their origins and extent, infanticide and abortion in past times and among various contemporary cultures can hardly be looked upon as conscious means of effecting population control. Rare societies, particularly societies confined to small islands, like the Tikopia, may have been aware of the necessity of limiting their numbers. But for the most part the limitations are clearly matters of personal and family convenience. A small family pattern is established under conditions where large families would be a handicap; and where large families are an asset, as in many sorts of agricultural economies, large families become prevalent.

This remains true today of the contraceptive practices that have become so widespread in our modern Western civilization. The couple planning to have one child, or two, or three, are not thinking of the Malthusian problem of population and resources, but of their own situation, of the expense of educating many children, of the drudgery of caring for infants, of the interference with careers or cherished activities. The propaganda of the birth control organizations has this slant; it emphasizes the gain in health and convenience of planned parenthood, rather than the economic danger of a recklessly multiplying human species.

The birth control movement, however, certainly had its beginnings in a Malthusian climate of opinion. Malthus himself seems to have clung to the hope that "moral restraint," that is, delayed marriage, would resolve the dilemma he so vividly expounded. His reasoning about the nature of the problem, however, convinced many of his contemporaries that other means of population control would have to be found, and thus gave an intellectual basis to their interest in the spread of contraceptive practices.

The first open advocacy of contraception as a check to overpopulation in England was a book by Francis Place, published in 1822, called *Some Illustrations of the Principles of Population.* This was followed by many other books, pamphlets and handbills, but the movement gained no real momentum in England until 1877 when Charles Bradlaugh and Mrs. Annie Besant challenged a court decision by reprinting and selling copies of a book by an American, Dr. Charles Knowlton, called *The Fruits of Philosophy.* "Their trial and subsequent appeal attracted nationwide attention, and everywhere family limitation became a subject of public discussion. For the first time birth control propaganda made headway. Branches of the Malthusian League were formed in many towns, and from many parts of the country there came requests from trade unions and other bodies for lectures and literature on family limitation. The sales of Dr. Knowlton's book in Great Britain jumped from about 1,000 a year before the trial to more than 200,000 in the 3½ years following it." (Quotation from the Report of the Royal Commission on Population.)

There was nothing in the United States corresponding to the English Malthusian League until 1917, when the National Birth Control League was founded. There was, however, plenty of interest in the matter earlier, and a considerable volume of publication, both popular and medical. The first American book on birth control was published in 1830, *Moral Physiology* by Robert Dale Owen. The second (in 1832) was Knowlton's *The Fruits of Philosophy,* which caused so much trouble when imported into England.

The early writers on birth control in America also encountered legal difficulties; and in 1873 a federal statute was passed, the so-called Comstock law, prohibiting the distribution of contraceptive information through the mails. Dr. Edward Foote was indicted under this law in 1876 for mailing a copy of a pamphlet called *Words in Pearl.* He was found guilty and fined $3,000 with costs of some $5,000. This law long continued to be rigidly interpreted, creating a situation in the United States quite different from that in England, where the Bradlaugh-Besant trial of 1877 went far toward making legal the general, free distribution of contraceptive knowledge.

Birth control knowledge certainly continued to spread in the United States, legal or not, and Norman Himes has analyzed a considerable volume of American publication in his book on the history of the subject. The chief effect of the law was probably to delay the spread of information to the poorest economic classes, where the need would have been the greatest. The process of "democratization" of birth control in the United States made little headway until Margaret Sanger injected her personality into the movement in 1912. Her work as a nurse in the poor quarters of the lower East Side in New York convinced her that something ought to be done about bringing contraceptive information to poor mothers. She wrote a pamphlet called *Family Limitation* which was issued surreptitiously, but which got into legal difficulties. In 1916, she opened a birth control clinic in the Brownsville section of Brooklyn. This was closed by the police as a "public nuisance." Eventually, however, a decision of the Court of Appeals on this case opened up the possibility of the establishment of clinics where medical personnel could legally give contraceptive advice "for the cure and prevention of disease." Disease, fortunately, is a word susceptible of broad interpretation.

The studies that have been carried out by numerous social scientists in America and the various countries of Western Europe leave no room to doubt that the spread of contraception is primarily responsible for the declining birth rates in these countries in modern times. There is no evidence for a decline in reproductive capacity on a scale required to explain the statistics. The nervous strain of contemporary industrial civilization may be having some effect on fecundity—at least there is an increasing preoccupation with problems of sterility on the part of the medical profession—but this effect, if it exists at all, must be slight. Abortions are probably fairly common, but there is no way of making even an intelligent guess about the incidence of such an illegal activity. There is no reason to suppose, however, that it has an effect on the birth rate in any way comparable to that of contraception in Western countries. As the British Royal Commission reported, all of the evidence leads to the same conclusion, "that the great majority of married couples nowadays practice some form of birth control in order to limit their families, and that they are successful, not in the sense that birth control never fails, but in the sense that it reduces the number of conceptions considerably below the number that would otherwise take place."

Contraceptive practice is not, of course, uniformly distributed through the married population. In Western countries there are significant differences among the various economic classes, and between the Protestant and Roman Catholic religious groups. The difference in fertility in different income groups is a matter of common observation—and also a subject of detailed study by many population experts. There has long been some difference in family size among economic classes, due to differences in marriage habits—the professional and administrative classes tending to marry later than the manual laborers. But it also seems clear that modern contraceptive practices were first adopted by the more educated and more well to do. The gradual spread of the small family pattern down to the lower economic groups has been particularly well documented for England in the Report of the Royal Commission. The authors of this report see, in the contemporary scene, a new element in that it is becoming fashionable now for the upper income groups to have slightly larger families, and they wonder whether this practice too will gradually percolate through the lower economic strata by a process of emulation.

There is quite a deal of research being carried out on the

problems of contraception, some of it direct; more of it is indirect, on the general problems of the physiology of reproduction. We have a great deal yet to learn about the physiology of
sex, and about the human behavior patterns that govern reproduction; but it also seems to me, from a rather superficial survey
of the literature, that we have acquired a great deal of basic
information, enough perhaps to warrant more concentration on
the practical problem of finding more efficient contraceptive
techniques. Some of the pharmaceutical houses are carrying out
interesting research programs in this field, in the hope of improving their products and of finding new products that they can sell.
This is fine; but it seems to me also that the problem calls for
work of a noncommercial sort, under disinterested auspices.
Unfortunately, in the United States the whole subject is still in
a sort of halfway taboo state, so that governmental organizations,
foundations and universities are afraid to sponsor such work
because of its "controversial" nature.

There was, at one time, a great deal of objection to public
health measures, like vaccination, because of interference with
the "will of God." Control of the agencies of death, however,
has become an accepted part of our culture, and we have made
extraordinary progress in lowering the hazards of life during
infancy and through the years when the adult is reproducing. It
seems to me perfectly plain that this interference with mortality
must be balanced by interference with natality, lest we endanger
all of the varied social, cultural and technical gains that have
been associated with our control of mortality.

But before pursuing this line of thought, we should examine
the factors that govern mortality in man.

CHAPTER *8* THE CAUSES OF DEATH

In the United States 1,452,454 people died in 1950, which works out as an average of 9.6 deaths for every thousand inhabitants. Almost a third of these deaths were caused by heart disease (2.7 per thousand), with cancer (1.4 per thousand) next, followed by cerebral hemorrhage, accidents, nephritis, pneumonia, tuberculosis, infant deaths (premature), diabetes and arteriosclerosis in that order.

The picture of death in the United States in 1950, however, was quite different from that for most of the world, or for most of human history. The United States did not have the lowest death rate in the world—that distinction belonged to the Netherlands in 1950, with 7.5 deaths per thousand inhabitants; and death rates in Australia, New Zealand, the Netherlands and some of the Scandanavian countries have generally been slightly lower than in the United States during recent years. But death in the United States, in western Europe and in the British Dominions has taken on a new aspect during the present century. It is no less inevitable for each of us; but it has been postponed, and with this postponement, it has come to operate through new agents—degenerative diseases instead of infectious diseases.

This modern shift is well documented. In the United States in 1900, for instance, an average of 17.2 deaths occurred for every thousand inhabitants, and the leading cause was tuberculosis, with pneumonia and infant diarrhea in second and third place. Heart disease was in fourth place and cancer in eighth place.

When we start to compare conditions in the United States in 1950, or in 1900, with conditions in the non-Western world, or with conditions in the past, we come up against the problem of statistics. For most of the past, and for most of the non-Western present, they simply aren't available, because detailed statistics, like the postponement of death, are a phenomenon of the modern Western world.

The death rate in India in 1950, according to the statistics, was 16.0 per thousand inhabitants; but a government committee, studying the matter, concluded that anywhere from 35 per cent to 55 per cent of the deaths were unreported. There are about 6,300 people for every physician in India, as compared with 750 people per physician in the United States. Under these circumstances, there is no possibility of accurately diagnosing the exact cause of death in the vast majority of cases—a problem that is difficult enough, even when physicians are abundant. Certainly, however, the major cause of death is infectious disease, with plague, cholera, malaria and smallpox probably leading the list.

Famine and war do not appear on the statistical summaries put out by the agencies of modern government—"statistics from the armed services" are usually specifically excluded. Yet both have long been major causes of human deaths—and neither has been eliminated. There are, of course, statistics in abundance on the modern wars of Western states, and we can make some kind of guess about the frequency of wars and their toll in human lives for other times and other civilizations. On famine, too, we have some statistics and many estimates. War, famine and disease, because of their importance and because of their implications, warrant examination in separate chapters. Before taking these up, let's try to look at death as a general phenomenon.

Death, like reproduction, is a universal property of life; indeed, it might be regarded as a necessary consequence of reproduction.

When we think of death—or reproduction—we are generally thinking in terms of the individual organism. But the matter of ends and beginnings can be examined at many other levels. Individuals die, but life itself, as far as we can observe it, is a continuing process. The life stuff, the protoplasm, is immortal in that the new individual starts from the germ cells of antecedent individuals; and each individual has at least the potentiality of immortality through his own germ cells. If life had a beginning, it presumably will have an end, but the beginning lies outside the area that we have been able to observe and the end will surely be beyond our observation.

The life stuff is not organized at random into individuals, but into a multiplicity of kinds of organisms, into different species, each of which, at any given cross section of time, has its germ materials isolated from that of others by the sexual process. A species is a population of organisms that do or could interbreed with one another, but that are separated from other similar organisms by reproductive barriers.

All of biology bears witness to the relatedness of species, to the origin of new species from pre-existing species. The fossils of the rocks have left us fragmentary records of this process going back, back through dizzy millions and billions of years to the earliest of the sedimentary rocks. We get glimpses from this record of an endless parade of kinds of organisms, of the appearance of new species and types and the disappearance of old. The diversity becomes greater as we approach more recent times, and we can see that, from time to time, radically new kinds of organization for life appear—insects, seed plants, fish, reptiles, mammals. These major types, once established, have almost always persisted, and we see the result today in the bewildering variety of organic form from bacteria and viruses to orchids and elephants.

The species, however, have come and gone with a fair sort of regularity. A particular, specific kind of organism has sometimes persisted through a quite long stretch of geological time, but the average time span is something like a million years. Within that time a given species either disappears, becomes extinct, or changes into something recognizably different, presumably better adapted to the ever-shifting conditions of life on the planetary surface.

Man is a species of animal. Presumably, then, he will presently become extinct or else slowly change into something recognizably different. In one way, man is a quite new phenomenon on the earth, because of his development of culture. We have no reason to suppose, however, that cultural evolution has replaced biological evolution with the human species—it seems rather to be superimposed upon the biological processes. Extinction or biological change, then, remain probabilities—but again presumably for a future calculable in terms of geological time.

The course of cultural evolution in man has produced a diversity of societies and civilizations which are in many ways analogous with the species and genera of biological evolution. With these societies and cultures we can again see the processes of change, of extinction, of divergence and parallelism—only now on a scale of historical time rather than geological time. This gives these processes an immediacy that puts them in a quite different category from events that happen with geological time. The extinction of our species seems to me a matter of interesting speculation about some possibly remote and unlikely occurrence. But the extinction of our civilization has nothing of this academic, abstract character.

Our historians have long been preoccupied with this business of the rise, flowering and decline of civilizations, but their researches have shown little regularity in the process. There is a temptation to make comparisons with the individual in terms like youth, maturity and senility. I don't think a civilization is like an individual; it is more like a species. We can calculate from the past a sort of average duration for either species or civilizations, and we can deduce that no species and no civilization will last forever. But there is no demonstrable inherent internal rhythm or cycle in either case. Civilizations like those of Egypt and China have shown an extraordinary persistence, while others have flourished only briefly and disappeared.

It is very hard for us to realize the inevitability of our own death and perhaps even harder to realize the possible extinction of our civilization, of our way of life. The possibility with our civilization, though, has been vividly enough before us for some years; and in this case, there is the tantalizing conviction that if we could only act wisely, the inevitable might be staved off. More than that, if we could act wisely, we might be on the verge of a new and glorious period in which man could move on toward that perfection glimpsed by the French philosophers. But how are we to find the way of wisdom? I don't know— except that I am sure we won't find it by refusing to think about it or by refusing to make cultural adaptations to the changing circumstances of the world. If there is any lesson in the analogy between species and civilizations, it is that survival depends on adaptability to change.

When we turn from the species or the society to the individual, we find a new idea, that of "natural death." By this I suppose we mean the death that occurs when the time clock that seems to be built into each of us runs down. Death, in this sense, is a property of the organization of the parts that go to make up the individual. Particular tissues, taken from the animal or plant and grown in laboratory flasks, may live indefinitely as long as anyone is around to take care of them, to provide nutrients and to prevent overcrowding.

Yet each system of tissue organization, each kind of individual organism, seems to have a characteristic life span. The shortest life spans would be among the single-celled organisms, which are constantly dying and constantly reproducing, so that generations are measured in minutes and hours. Some of these, too, may have the longest life spans, when they go into spore forms, where life may be maintained apparently indefinitely— certainly for years; whether for thousands of years I don't know.

Of multicellular organisms, the longest lives occur among plants. Some of these seem to have no time clock built in— they go on living and growing until some catastrophe, some change of climate, some force from the world outside brings an end to the individual. Of this sort are the famous sequoias which, when cut by man, show clearly in the record of the annual rings of growth that they started out their individual existence a thousand, two thousand years ago.

Some of the baobab trees of Cape Verde are said to be 5,000 years old. At the other extreme are all of the hosts of annual plants that bloom, fruit and die, completing their life span in a matter of weeks or months.

Among animals, some of the fish seem not to have a definite life span. Carp have been known to live for 150 years, and pike up to 200. Some reptiles, too, seem to live indefinitely, and the longevity of turtles and crocodiles is notorious. Among birds, parrots have been known to live 80 years, eagles 100.

Large size is not a sure sign of great age. The largest of all animals is the blue whale (which may weigh up to 125 tons, and reach a length of 115 feet). We do not know certainly how long these animals may live, but we do know that they grow rapidly. The calves, when born, weigh 8 tons and are 25 feet long. They double in size in a year, and become sexually mature in three years.

The best statistics on length of life, of course, are for man himself, but even these hardly allow us to be very definite about the "natural" life span for the species. Clearly, men rarely live beyond 100 years. A survey of over 800,000 life insurance cases in Great Britain, which would presumably have accurate records, yielded only 22 instances in which the 100 year mark was passed. Raymond Pearl, the American biologist, collected records of 497 centenarians, but not all of these were authenticated.

The extreme of longevity among moderns seems to belong to a Dane named Christen Jacobsen Drakenberg, who was born on the 18th of November, 1626, and died on the 9th of October, 1772—which means he lived 146 years. Dublin, Lotka and Spiegelman have discussed this case in their book called *Length of Life*. Drakenberg was an active fellow, who went to sea at the age of 13, fought in several wars, was captured by pirates and kept as a slave for fifteen years, escaping to take part in a war between the Danes and the Swedes at the age of 84, and marrying, at the age of 111, a widow aged 60. He was said to be sturdy, robust, and very impetuous!

"Natural death" must be unusual in "nature" because the whole complex system of kinds of organisms is built on one thing killing (and eating) another, so that it is only under the unnatural conditions of carefully protected captivity that we have a chance of watching the time clock run down in different kinds of organisms. Death ordinarily then is a consequence of the organization of the biological community, rather than a consequence of the internal organization of the individual.

Biologists distinguish between the ideas of *physiological* longevity and *ecological* longevity much as they distinguish between potential reproductive capacity (fecundity) and actual reproductive rate (fertility). The physiological longevity for a given kind of organism would be the average length of life of individuals of that kind under optimum conditions, where external or environmental causes of death were excluded. The ecological longevity would be the average length of life of individuals under the various conditions in which that kind of organism actually lives.

With man in the Western world, we are reaching conditions where the ecological longevity approaches the physiological. Medical science has so far made no progress in solving the problems of physiological longevity; its success has been with ecological longevity, with the various sorts of external conditions, especially disease, that so frequently intervene before the time clock has run down. This postponement of death will be dealt with in a later chapter.

Average longevity, of course, is a sort of converse of the death rate; though it is hard to relate the two concepts without getting thoroughly entangled with statistical methods. Mortality is ordinarily dealt with in terms of the "crude death rate" in terms of number of deaths per thousand population per year. The crude death rate in the United States for the last 15 years or so has been about ten per thousand. Now if ten persons per thousand die every year in a stable population, the average age of death, or average longevity, ought to be one hundred years; and this obviously isn't true. The average age at death in the United States during this same period was somewhere around 60 instead of around 100. The difference, of course, is due to the fact that the population was not stable, but constantly growing, thus upsetting the relation between length of life and age at death.

The analysis of mortality is more meaningful if it is carried out in terms of specific death rates: death rates for particular age groups, for economic or social groups, for particular diseases. The death rates of males and females show significant differences. On the average, there are about 105 males born for every 100 females, but male death rates are higher from the beginning, and in old-age groups, females are considerably in excess.

"Life expectancy" is calculated from the age-specific death rates; and the importance of this subject for insurance purposes has led to a great deal of work on methods of making life tables showing expectation of life for people at different ages, sometimes according to place of residence, occupation, and so forth. In this matter of the changing death rates with the development of medicine and public health, it is interesting that expectation of life at birth has changed greatly in the United States; but the expectation of life for older groups has changed less. Life expectancy at birth in Massachusetts in 1850 was about 40 years; in 1950 it was about 66 years. But in 1850, a person who had reached the age of 60 in Massachusetts could expect, on the average, to live 15 years longer—and in 1950, he could expect to live about 17 years longer! Similarly, while life expectancy at birth today is very different in different parts of the earth, life expectancy at 60 is about the same for all countries where the statistics are good enough to allow calculation. A large part of the difference in life expectancy at birth in different countries is due to infant mortality, and the most striking achievements of medicine and public health have been in lowering the death rate in the first year of life. In the United States in 1950, 29 out of every thousand infants died before they were a year old. This, in the range of known human experience, is a very low figure. In 1900, in the United States, 162 of every thousand infants died in the first year of life. Over a good part of the world the infant mortality rate even in 1950 was somewhere around 200 per thousand live births—a fifth or more of all babies dying in the first year of life.

The young of all animals are particularly exposed to the

hazards of existence. In some cases, as with many marine organisms, survival seems to be merely a matter of chance: millions of offspring are produced so that one or two may survive. If we regarded spermatozoa as offspring, this would still be true in man. The figures I quoted in the chapter on reproduction, of 185 million spermatozoa in an ejaculate, and 351 copulations for each conception, would multiply out to mean that only one human spermatozoan in 65 billion had a chance to perpetuate itself.

Among most animals the young, on hatching from the egg or after birth from the mother, must fend for themselves. The exceptions, where some degree of parental care is exercised, are rare and sporadic except among the social insects, the birds and the mammals. Among mammals the newborn is always dependent on the mother for food, and in most cases is incapable even of walking. The newborn human infant is no more helpless than the newborn of many other mammals; though the young of man is dependent on the parents for longer than that of any other animal.

The chances of a human infant dying in the second year of life are very much less than in the first year, and the age-specific mortality rates go down with each succeeding year to reach their lowest point at ten years. At this point the special hazards of infancy have been passed, and the hazards of adult life have not yet started. When tuberculosis was a leading cause of death, mortality showed a considerable increase in the late teens and early twenties, due chiefly to this disease.

The chances of death, then, are greatest in the periods of infancy and old age, least in the period of adolescence. This seems to be very generally true, even though the amount of infant mortality varies greatly in different circumstances, as does the age at which death again becomes an ever-present threat.

One of the peculiarities of man is that he frequently outlives his biological usefulness—or perhaps I should have written *her* usefulness, since I was thinking of the menopause of the female. This definite age limit on reproduction, preceding by many years other senile phenomena, is peculiar to the human species. Other mammals occasionally outlive their reproductive ability, but they seem not to have the regularity in the suspension of the reproductive processes of the human female. The human male is less unusual in this respect, since the decline in reproductive ability is gradual, with, apparently, considerable individual difference.

I suppose one might consider that an individual who has passed his reproductive usefulness is biologically, or physiologically, "dead," which brings us back to the difference between physiological longevity and ecological longevity that I mentioned earlier. The menopause and the increasing impotence of the aging male are two examples of a whole series of degenerative processes that set in as the clock of the individual runs down. We are getting more and more interested in these processes of aging as we get larger and larger numbers of old people in our populations, and the study of aging has come to be the field of a special science called geriatrics.

But it is only as we have conquered ecological death, death from causes external to the nature of the organism, that we have come clearly to recognize this physiological death, death that seems to be a property of the way the organism is organized, and we are still a long way from understanding or controlling it. With organisms in general, and surely also with man through most of his evolution, the causes of death have been ecological—factors of the environment in which the organism lives.

In trying to study the causes of death of organisms in nature, biologists have come to distinguish between two broad classes of factors which they call *density dependent* and *density independent*. A great many organisms fall victims to what we might call accidents of the physical environment—a sudden frost, or

the regular frost that marks the beginning of winter, a prolonged
drought, a flood, a hurricane. Such catastrophes are quite independent of the numbers of animals present in a population;
they are density independent. Immense numbers of field mice
living in the countryside near the Mississippi may be killed by
a flood of the river; but the flood is not caused by the over-
abundance of field mice.

An epidemic disease, in this respect, is quite different from a
flood. So long as mice are rare and widely scattered, there is little
opportunity for a disease to spread through the population. But
as numbers build up, as mice become more and more common,
come in contact with one another more and more frequently, the
chances for contagion increase, and presently a catastrophe may
occur that is essentially made possible by the abundance of the
mice. The mortality, in this case, is density dependent.

The study of mortality, from this ecological point of view, is
obviously important for an understanding of the "balance of
nature," the equilibrium of the biotic community. Ecological
death to a very large extent seems to be density dependent—
as rabbits multiply, the foxes that live on them multiply—so
that there is a sort of automatic adjustment to prevent an extreme of overcrowding. Such density relationships must have
applied to man over much of the period of his evolution, and
our present spurt of multiplication could be looked at as an
escape—perhaps temporary—from such controls.

We might classify the ecological causes of death in man under
such headings as predation, parasitism, food failure, accident
and murder.

Predation is probably the commonest cause of death among
animals in general because of the whole food-chain system. Only
the top predators—the lions, hawks, crocodiles and men—
escape; and they may be prey themselves, especially while young.
Predation is an extremely rare cause of death with man today.
There is the occasional Asian villager who falls victim to a

man-eating tiger, or the African picked up by a crocodile while bathing in a Nile tributary, or the swimmer seized by a shark. Such deaths cause enough stir in the communities where they occur, but they could hardly be regarded as a limiting factor in population even among the most defenseless of contemporary human societies.

I suspect that predation has never been an important cause of death in man, puny and weak as he seems in comparison with the big cats and other predators of the Pleistocene. If we assume that man's ancestors were social before they were human, the physical defenselessness of the individual would be more than offset by the advantages of the socially cooperating group. This seems to be true today even of the small social monkeys. Carpenter, from his study of the howler monkeys in Panama, felt that the only ones that fell victim to the big cats were the individuals that strayed from the groups.

Parasitism, on the other hand, has certainly been the most important cause of death in man, at least in historic times—the sort of parasitism that we call infectious disease. It is possible to get into all sorts of trouble in trying to distinguish between parasitism and predation because there is every sort of gradation in the way animals live off each other, from the lion that uses a sheep for a meal or two to the worm that snuggles contentedly for life in the sheep's liver. But in the case of things that live off man, there is a fairly clear distinction between the big ones that kill him all at once and the little ones that kill him gradually. The relation between parasites—or infectious disease—and human population warrants exploration in a separate chapter.

This predation-parasite business works two ways: man may serve as food for something else, thereby encountering death; but he must also find food for himself, thereby causing the death of other organisms. And if he fails to find food, he will himself die by the process we call starvation.

It seems to me that death through starvation, through failure to find food, is relatively uncommon in nature; though it would be hard to get any statistics on the subject. It is easy, in fact, looking at a meadow or forest or pond, to be impressed by the amount of food that is "going to waste," especially if one is looking from the point of view of some particular kind of animal. There always seems to be plenty of grass for the rabbits, and plenty of rabbits for the hawks. When the population of some particular species does increase enormously, for some reason, so that it passes the limits of its food supply, the result is often a general catastrophe with effects that go far beyond the particular species that is first to go out of bounds. Starvation, then, instead of being an agency of death for isolated individuals, becomes an agency of death for whole populations or large parts of them. This epidemic starvation we call famine— a subject that will be examined in a separate chapter.

Ecological death is not always a consequence of being food for something else, or of failing to get food for one's self—there are also accidents. It would be interesting if one could reconstruct the history of accidents in human mortality, and get some idea of their role in human evolution. Was "accidental death" particularly common among those Stone Age ancestors of ours, and did keenness of eye and sureness of foot thus gain greatly in "survival value?" Or were such gains canceled out by a higher mortality among the adventurous in spirit, giving "survival value" to the conservatives who stuck by the old and the tried?

Accidental death, in recent years at least, has been steadily increasing in importance; and there is a direct relation between the increase in accidental death and the increasing complexity and deadliness of the gadgets of our civilization—particularly automobiles. Accidents in the United States were ninth in rank as a cause of death in 1900, and fourth in rank in recent years. One can see a steady climb in the figures: 90,106 accidental deaths in 1949; 91,249 in 1950; 95,500 in 1951; 96,000 in

1952. The big increase, of course, is always in the special category of "motor vehicle accidents" which, in 1952, caused 38,000 of the deaths and an additional 1,350,000 injuries of varying severity.

The most curious of the causes of death in man, however, are those in which man is the agency of his own death—murder, homicide, suicide, war. It seems to me there ought to be some special collective word that would cover all of these slightly variant ways in which man manages to kill himself. It is such a special phenomenon that it surely warrants a special word. "Homicide" or "suicide" won't do because of their established meanings. I put the problem to a friend who is a Greek scholar, thinking that we might get a proper word by shifting from Latin roots to Greek roots. He suggested *anthropoktony,* which is certainly horrendous enough.

Anthropoktony takes a bewildering variety of forms and seems almost to be built into human ecology. Perhaps as man, in the course of evolution, escaped the more usual forms of population control, anthropoktony developed to fill the gap—since other things didn't kill man often enough to keep his mortality in line with his reproduction, he had to take to killing himself. But it seems a most peculiar solution to the population problem.

I have been trying to think how one could develop a neat classification of the varieties of anthropoktony. We might distinguish solitary anthropoktony and social anthropoktony—as we distinguish between solitary and social insects. The solitary kind would be where one individual kills another individual for private reasons, and would include also the cases where an individual deliberately kills himself—the special case of suicide. Social anthropoktony would involve group action. This is the most effective kind from the population point of view, since large numbers of people can kill large numbers of other people quite quickly, particularly with some of our modern techniques.

Social anthropoktony doesn't necessarily involve large scale action, though. I suppose family feuds could be called social. In such cases members of one family pick off members of another family and vice versa at intervals over many years; and the actual number of deaths may be statistically rather insignificant, especially when viewed in terms of the breeding activities of the same feuding families.

I am not sure, in this classification, what to do with the cases where a society kills an individual because he has bad habits or bad ideas—the variety of anthropoktony that we call "execution." I suppose this is social anthropoktony, since the whole society sanctions the killing, even though it may be only a single individual that is killed. The same principle can, of course, be applied for large scale killings, as was the policy of Nazi Germany, or some of the medieval dealings with heresy.

Solitary anthropoktony can seem rather trivial when compared with varieties of social anthropoktony like war and genocide, but even the solitary sorts account for considerable numbers of human deaths. In 1952, for instance, there were 16,030 suicides in the United States, and 8,240 homicides. Both are widespread human customs, with all sorts of interesting implications for the student of culture or human behavior, and the United States is not particularly outstanding for either its suicide or its homicide rate.

For real population effects, however, we have to turn to social anthropoktony, which forms the subject of the next chapter.

CHAPTER *9* MAN AGAINST MAN

War and famine and disease—those are the words around which one must organize any discussion of human mortality. And of these, war now seems the most important, the most insoluble. This vaunted Western civilization of ours can list, as its proudest accomplishments, the mitigation of hunger and disease. They are still potent and awful forces in the world; but at least within the West itself, we have gained confidence that we can deal with them as we learn how to multiply and store and transport our food, how to maintain an economy of abundance, how to deal with one after another of the diseases that have caused mankind so much pain and misery.

But just when we seem to have the abundant life and the healthy life within our reach, the shadow of war grows ever darker and more ominous. It makes our other gains seem almost trivial, almost pointless. Science, which has given us so much help with food and disease, here seems to have become our enemy, giving us only more powerful and more dreadful agencies of destruction.

We have, of course, no business blaming science for our failure to solve the problem of war. War belongs to the area of human relations, and if science is going to be helpful there, it will at least be a different kind of science from the kind that has produced thermonuclear weapons. Science, in the development of the instruments of war, has served only to change the scale of human actions, not to influence the nature of the actions themselves. The change in scale, however, makes it imperative that we find some solution to the problems of the human (or political) actions themselves.

Much paper and ink has been expended in the discussion of the origins of war, of whether warring behavior is an essential component of human nature. War has even been defended as a "good thing" because it promoted national unity and vigor, because it was in accord with the grand natural principles of the struggle for existence and survival of the fittest. By such processes war can be justified, condemned, or explained—depending largely on whether the particular author is more impressed by the competitive or by the cooperative aspects of nature, on whether he takes as his unit the individual man, the nation, or mankind as a whole.

I have never been able to see that this sort of discussion has much relevance to the solution of the contemporary problem of war. Whatever the biological origins of war, or whether it has biological origins, it is now a social or cultural problem and must be dealt with as such. War, as we know it, is a product of cultural evolution, not of biological evolution. Therein lies our hope, because biological changes take place in the time scale of geological history, whereas cultural changes involve the very different scale of human history. History sometimes seems painfully slow, but it can also move with dramatic speed. Peace may not be a part of human nature; but surely neither is flying. It seems incredible that it should be more difficult for man to learn to live in peace with his fellow-men than it was for man to learn to fly.

Quincy Wright, in his book *A Study of War,* defines war as the "legal condition which equally permits two or more hostile groups to carry on a conflict by armed force." Or in a variant phrasing, as the "condition or period of time in which special rules permitting and regulating violence between governments prevail."

This is the concept of civilized war (what a curious combination of words!). It is a phenomenon of government, and its origins would thus be bound up in the origins of government. Governments commonly feel that the rules of war have no application when dealing, not with other governments, but with such aggregations of people as "native tribes" or rebellious subjects. The use of force in such instances may be called a "police action." Armed strife between native tribes may be put in the special category of "primitive war."

A fight between two individuals seems never to be called war; nor are squabbles among families, however bloody. Individual violence represents a fight, family violence a feud, and war is thus restricted, even in its broadest sense, to intergroup violence. Here, however, from the point of view of population, we might as well lump the whole business of man as a direct agent of death for man, whether by individual or group action.

This suicidal mania, this intraspecific killing, seems to be a peculiarly human characteristic. One can, of course, find all sorts of biological parallels, but they are sporadic and trivial or fundamentally different from the human phenomenon. With a few organisms, some of the young eat each other to get a start in life. With some animals, such as mantids and spiders, the female may eat the male—but after fertilization is accomplished, when the male is no longer of any biological use, anyway. Cannibalism occurs among many sorts of animals when they are crowded in laboratory cages or aquaria, but generally this is clearly a result of the artificial confinement. Fights among males over a female in heat are common enough in a wide variety of animals, but only rarely are these fatal to any of the contenders.

Some species of ants raid the nests of other ants, and even make "slaves" by capturing pupae which are taken home to hatch into workers for the raiding colony. But these raids are by ants of one species on ants of another species—biologically a very different phenomenon from human warfare within the species. The extreme of organized ferocity is probably reached by the famous army ants of the tropics; but again they are warring against all animals except those of their own kind.

Yet man's ferocity to man does have one clear biological counterpart in territoriality. If war has any innate, "instinctive" basis, it may most likely be found to be a derivative of the reactions associated with defense of territory, so widely characteristic of the vertebrates.

Territory, in the biological sense, is generally defined as an area defended against competing members of the same species. With social mammals, the territory is the property of the group, herd or clan, and is defended against intrusion by individual outsiders or by other groups. Territoriality, as I have pointed out, must have many implications in human evolution, and it may be well to examine it again here from the particular point of view of strife within the species.

It is interesting, in this connection, to look at the behavior of the social canines, the dogs and wolves, because these form hunting packs. Various authors have suggested that man may well have gone through a hunting pack stage in his social evolution, and that some of the similarities between canine behavior and human behavior may be explained on this basis. Contemporary social primates are mostly a peaceable lot, predominantly vegetarian or insectivorous, and in this respect they may differ from the protohominids—who certainly were carnivorous in some cases, as certainly also were some of the Pleistocene human hunting cultures.

Unfortunately, it is not easy to make observations on the social behavior of wolves in the wild. It is clear that they normally travel in packs, and while these sometimes consist of a single family, they perhaps more usually include several families, several cooperating adult males. The finest study so far made of wolf behavior is by Adolph Murie, who worked in the region of Mt. McKinley. The "East Fork pack," which he was able to watch, consisted of three adult males and two females, the latter each with litters of five pups. His observations on the attempts of a strange wolf to join this pack make a convincing demonstration that wolves, as well as men, can be mean to each other.

An incident at the East Fork den indicates the treatment that a strange wolf may receive. On May 31, 1940, all five adults were at home. Between 10 A.M. and noon the mantled male had been on the alert, raising his head to look around at intervals of 2 or 3 minutes. Several times he changed his position until he was about 200 yards above the den. Such prolonged watchfulness was unusual, but it was explained by later events. Shortly after noon the four wolves at the den joined the mantled male and they all bunched up, wagging tails and expressing much friendliness. Then I noticed a sixth wolf, a small grey animal, about 50 yards from the others. No doubt the presence of this wolf had kept the mantled male so alert during the preceding 2 hours.

All the wolves trotted to the stranger and practically surrounded it, and for a few moments I thought that they would be friendly toward it for there was just the suggestion of tail wagging by some of them. But something tipped the scales the other way for the wolves began to bite at the stranger. It rolled over on its back, begging quarter. The attack continued, however, so it scrambled to its feet and with difficulty emerged from the snapping wolves. Twice it was knocked over as it ran down the slope with the five wolves in hot pursuit. They chased after it about 200 yards to the river bar, and the mantled male crossed the bar after it. The two ran out of my sight under the ridge from which I was watching.

Four of the wolves returned to the den, but the mantled male stopped half way up the slope and lay down facing the bar. Presently he walked slowly forward as though stalking a marmot. Then he commenced to gallop down the slope again toward the stranger which had returned part way up the slope. Back on the bar the stranger slowed up, waiting in a fawning attitude for the mantled male. The latter snapped at the stranger which rolled over on its back, again begging for quarter. But the stranger received no quarter, so again it had to run away. The male returned up the hill, tail held stiffly out behind, slightly raised. When he neared the den the four wolves ran out to meet him, and there was again much tail wagging and evidence of friendly meeting.

The unfortunate stranger's hip and base of tail were soaked with blood. It was completely discouraged in its attempt to join the group, for it was not seen again. It may have been forced to leave the territory of this wolf family, for if it were encountered it probably would have been attacked again. Judging from the usual reaction of a group of dogs to a strange dog, such treatment of a strange wolf would seem normal. Small groups of wolves may be treated like this lone wolf, hence it is advantageous for minor packs to find territories where they are unmolested. Such rough treatment of individual wolves, if it is normal, would tend to limit the number of wolves on a given range.

Carpenter has described somewhat similar attempts of single males to join clans of howler monkeys, except that with the monkeys there was no actual bloodshed. In one instance, a persistent male finally succeeded in joining a clan—which must also happen with wolves.

There is, however, one vast difference between territorial squabbling and other intraspecific fighting in man and other animals: only in man does this fighting commonly lead directly to death. The wounded wolf described by Murie is about the extreme of injury, and in most cases, one or another of the individuals or groups gives way before much physical damage is done. An individual that cannot establish territorial or social relations with his own kind may be doomed, but the direct agency of death is not another individual of his own species.

Konrad Lorenz has explored this matter in his delightful book on animal behavior, *King Solomon's Ring*. He notes that "when, in the course of evolution, a species of animal develops a weapon which may destroy a fellow-member at one blow, then, in order to survive, it must develop, along with the weapon, a social inhibition to prevent a usage which could endanger the existence of the species."

Lorenz gives many examples of the submissive attitudes which, in a defeated animal, serve to inhibit a final, fatal blow by the winner. He notes that "the supplicant always offers to his adversary the most vulnerable part of his body, or, to be more exact, that part against which every killing attack is inevitably directed." Thus, at the end of a fight which he described between two wolves, "the older wolf has his muzzle close, very close against the neck of the younger, and the latter holds away his head, offering unprotected to his enemy the bend of his neck, the most vulnerable part of his whole body! Less than an inch from the tensed neck-muscles, where the jugular vein lies immediately beneath the skin, gleam the fangs of his antagonist from beneath the wickedly retracted lips." The abject submission of the loser seems to serve as an effective, instinctive block to a fatal conclusion of the fight. We can find traces of this in our own behavior, in the prostrate or bowed, unarmed, appeal for mercy—but with man, the "inner obstruction" to the fatal blow is not always effective.

As Lorenz points out, man has been acquiring his armaments through cultural evolution—so he will have to acquire his inhibitions through the same process. Therein, however, lies hope. The evolution of a canine tooth and the evolution of the innate inhibition that blocks its fatal use both require time on the geological scale; but the time required for the social control of a high-powered rifle should be of the same order of magnitude as the time required for the development of the rifle itself. Cultural evolution is certainly capable of developing inhibitions as powerful as those based on instinct—witness the whole collection of taboos—but with weapons of war the evolution of the armaments and of the controlling behavior seem to have got out of phase.

It is clear that man has been killing man for a very long time, whatever the biological origins of the habit. A remarkable number of the fossil bones that have survived from the Stone Age show that the individual met a violent death of a sort that could only have been inflicted by some fellow-man. Thus, in the case of Peking man (Sinanthropus), everyone of the skulls shows evidence of heavy blows, and the limb bones were all split open —something that only man would do, in search of marrow. The fossil evidence, as far as Peking man is concerned, seems to show that the principal cause of death was murder with cannibal intent.

Murder also seems to have been a leading cause of death with later Paleolithic man in China. Franz Weidenreich, in his study of "The Duration of Life of Fossil Man in China" gives a nice, scholarly description of the evidence. Of the skulls from the Upper Cave at Choukoutien, Weidenreich writes:

The first skull, that of an old man . . . displays a typical round depressed fracture on the left side above the temporal region. It must have been caused by a pointed implement. The second skull, probably that of a woman, shows a long and wide slit-like hole at the superior part of the left temporal region. This hole breaks through the wall of the skull from above downward giving the impression that it was caused by a spear-like implement piercing through the wall from above. In addition, the entire skull is crushed into numerous smaller and larger fragments still in their natural connections. At least two centers are distinguishable from which these fractures radiate, indicating that the crushing was produced by heavy blows from club-like implements. The third skull is likewise fractured but not broken into such numerous fragments as in the second one. Also in this the fragments are in place in natural arrangement, the markings of the blows being located at the frontal region of the left side. The fourth skull consists of only the frontal and two parietal bones. Here the injuries are represented by a large fractured and deeply depressed area corresponding to the frontal sinus, the splinters of the outside are still in place and those of the inner side form a far protruding elevation. Both parietal bones display a large fractured depression with a typically split interior table. In this instance clubs and a more pointed weapon must have been used.

Our sample of skeletons, of course, is small, and the chances of preservation may have been greater for men who were murdered and dragged into caves to be eaten at leisure than for men killed out in the open by lions or accidents or disease. But even so, it looks as though life had its grim aspects in that Old Stone Age.

It is a long jump from the evidence that man killed man in very early times to the idea that this had anything to do with territory. But the idea seems plausible chiefly because territory is the most obvious cause of intraspecific strife among non-human animals and thus the one most likely to lead to fatal fighting among human animals that had only recently taken up the cultural use of weapons.

Cannibalism might easily follow from the nature of in-group out-group relations among social mammals. An individual not belonging to the group or territory would be regarded as foreign, hardly more "human" than any other animal. Once killed, for territorial transgression or any other reason, there would be no point in allowing the meat to go to waste. A survey of the eating habits of modern man shows quite conclusively that there is no such thing as "instinctive" aversion to any food. Whether man eats man or not seems to be just as clearly a cultural trait as whether man eats dog, or cow, or rattlesnake, or any other digestible, nonpoisonous food.

Certain peoples, like the pre-Columbian Caribs of the West Indies, have taken to cannibalism as a way of life, and this may have been true of the inhabitants of the Choukoutien cave. I can hardly believe that cannibalism was a universal among early men, in the sense of hunting and killing other men as a major source of food, because surely in that case man would have succeeded in exterminating himself quite early. Cannibalism may, though, have been common enough to be an important cause of death.

The anthropologists have found examples of every imaginable kind of cannibalism among recent peoples. There are cultures that eat only friends, others that eat only enemies; cultures in which old people are eaten, others in which infants are eaten. Sometimes only certain members of the society, such as warriors or priests, can do the eating; sometimes the eating takes place only under special circumstances. There is no clear relation between cannibalism and availability of other food. Cannibalism may occur among starving groups of almost any culture (including our own), and cannibalism is habitual among some peoples who have an abundance of other food and thus eat man either for some ritual reason or because they like the taste.

Cannibalism is closely associated with human sacrifice—especially where the cannibalism is of a ritual kind. On the one hand, the eating of human flesh easily takes on a religious significance; and on the other, where men are sacrificed to the gods, the sacrifice may involve the eating of some part of the victim—most often, perhaps, his heart. Both cannibalism and human sacrifices are biological luxuries possible only for a population with a credit balance in reproduction.

Human sacrifice reached its most staggering proportions with the ancient Mexicans. "Scarcely any author," says Prescott, in the *History of the Conquest of Mexico,* "pretends to estimate the yearly sacrifices throughout the empire at less than twenty thousand, and some carry the figure as high as fifty thousand." The Aztec sacrificial victims were mostly prisoners of war—and wars were waged for the express purpose of capturing prisoners for sacrifice. The Aztec tactics, which aimed at capturing the enemy rather than killing him, put them at a considerable disadvantage in the fights with the Spaniards.

The sacrifice of first-born children has been a curiously widespread practice, found among a variety of cultures in many parts of the world. The sacrifice of the first-born is commonly explained as a method of promoting fecundity, though the effect would seem to be to lower fertility. The reasoning behind human sacrifice, however, is almost endlessly diverse, as has been so well documented in the writings of Sir James Frazer and Edward Westermarck.

There is reason to suppose that human sacrifice is not a very ancient human pastime. It seems to go with the stages of "barbarism" and "civilization," with the development of settlements and the acquisition of leisure for the elaboration of complicated religious ideas. It also seems to be a transitory stage, since the great civilizations of the past seem independently to have evolved through the sacrifice stage to the use of various sorts of substitute symbols or to some less bloody sort of religious ritual.

Slavery, too, seems to have been a recent and transitory phase of human development, though the evolution here was perhaps a matter of economics rather than ideas. The maintenance of captive slaves requires a settled and somewhat complicated way of life. With the development of agriculture and other forms of arduous "work," the utility of enslaving foreigners or enemies instead of killing them becomes obvious, and has been taken up by almost all people who have reached that economic stage. With further economic development, particularly with the adoption of steam and electric power for industry and mechanization for agriculture, slavery again becomes impractical—though the modern totalitarian states seem still to find a form of slavery useful.

Slavery probably originated as a by-product of war; where it became firmly implanted in the economic system, it was also frequently a cause of war, in that a slave society would continually need new supplies of slaves. But warfare—organized intergroup aggression—existed long before slavery became institutionalized, and has continued after slavery has been abandoned. Warfare seems to be one of the most persistent of human traits, and one that has perhaps been important in shaping population developments for a very long time.

"War" probably is a sort of wastebasket word that has caught a variety of rather different things. It is particularly dangerous to try to trace any direct line of evolution from possible territorial squabblings among Pleistocene food-gatherers to the organized ferocity of modern Western states with their complicated rituals of international "law" and violations thereof. About all that can be found in this spectrum, from the bashed skulls of Peking man to the atomic bombs of World War II, is the continuing history of intraspecific violence.

Quincy Wright, in his *Study of War,* included a survey of the war practices of 588 different primitive peoples. He recognized four basic varieties of war among these people: defensive, social, economic and political. Defensive war is the practice of people who fight only when attacked; such people have no military organization or special weapons and make spontaneous use of available tools and hunting weapons to defend themselves "but regard this necessity as a misfortune."

Social war (the commonest variety of primitive war) refers to the practice of people who do not have economic or political motives in fighting, but who have "customs dealing with military tactics, military weapons, the circumstances and formalities of warmaking and peacemaking, and the warriors consist of all men of the tribe trained in war mores from youth." The purpose of war is "blood revenge, religious duty, individual prestige, sport, or other social objective. It may on occasion involve considerable casualties in proportion to the population of the group and is characterized as cruel and bloody by some writers because prisoners are not taken."

Economic war refers to the practice of people who fight "to provide the economic needs of the group, such as women, slaves, cattle, tools, raw materials, and land. Such people usually have a system of military training in mass tactics and regard war as a necessary part of the tribe's economic activities."

Political war "refers to the practice of people who, in addition to other purposes, fight for political objectives, i.e., to maintain a ruling dynasty or class in power, to suppress rebellion or insurrection, and to expand political territory or control. Such people usually support standing armies. . . . Among them the military profession is usually regarded as especially honorable. People with such practices are on the verge of civilization, but writers usually classify them as primitive but very warlike."

Wright's analysis shows little relation between "warlikeness" and geography, climate, or race. By culture groupings, the hunters were the least warlike, the agriculturists intermediate, and the pastoral peoples most warlike. There was also a correlation with political organization: the peoples organized into "clans" being least warlike, those organized into "villages" more so, those with "tribes" still more warlike, and those organized into "states" most warlike of all.

These sorts of relationships lead Wright to make the generalization that "primitive warfare was an important factor in developing civilization. It cultivated virtues of courage, loyalty, and obedience; it created solid groups and a method for enlarging the area of these groups, all of which were indispensable to the creation of the civilization which followed." Wright quotes R. R. Marett as writing: "It is a commonplace of anthropology that at a certain stage of evolution—the half-way stage, so to speak—war is a prime civilizing agency; in fact, that, as Bagehot puts it, 'Civilization begins because the beginning of civilization is a military advantage.' "

War and civilization have certainly generally gone together; whether there is any cause-and-effect relationship between the two is another matter. It would seem to me likely that civilization developed in spite of war, rather than because of it, and that the development of warlike habits has as often arrested the evolution of a culture as promoted it.

The addiction to social warfare by primitive gardening cultures in many parts of the world seems a case in point. This institution is admirably adapted to the maintenance of a static, "balanced" population situation—and to the arresting of possible cultural development. This relation between warfare, population and cultural development among the Indians of eastern North America has been described by Professor A. L. Kroeber:

Of social factors, the most direct may be considered to have been warlike habits. Reference is not to systematic, decisive war leading to occasional great destructions but also to conquest, settlement, and periods of consolidation and prosperity. Of all this the Eastern tribes knew nothing. They waged war not for any ulterior or permanent fruits, but for victory; and its conduct and shaping were motivated, when not by revenge, principally by individual desire for personal status within one's society. It was warfare that was insane, unending, continuously attritional, from our point of view; and yet it was so integrated into the whole fabric of Eastern culture, so dominantly emphasized within it, that escape from it was well-nigh impossible. Continuance in the system became self-preservatory. The group that tried to shift its values from war to peace was almost certainly doomed to early extinction. This warfare, with its attendant unsettlement, confusion, destruction, and famines, was probably the most potent reason why population remained low in the East. It kept agriculture in the role of a contributor to subsistence instead of the basis of subsistence. On the other hand, such farming as was practiced yielded enough of added leisure, concentration, and stability to make pretty continuous warfare possible. A population of pure hunter-gatherers would probably, except on the immediate coast, have been too scattered in minute bands, too unsettled in a country of rather evenly distributed food possibilities, too occupied with mere subsistence, to have engaged in war very persistently. Just this seems to have happened among Montagnais, Cree, and Ojibwa, for instance, as compared with Muskogians, Iriquoins, and Siouans. The latter were caught in a vicious circle, which at the same time gave them a stable adjustment. Agriculture made their wars possible; but their warfare kept the population down to a point where more agriculture was not needed.

It is probable, then, that through much of the period of cultural evolution, intraspecific strife has been an important limiting factor on the growth of human population. When we come to modern times and historic wars, the effect, curiously, is far less clear. There is, in fact, a widely held theory that war has little influence on the growth of population, and this theory is based mostly on observation of the actual statistical effects of the last two world wars.

It is very difficult to assess the effect of historic wars on population because so many factors are involved. Through most of history, the battle casualties have clearly been less important than the environmental disruptions accompanying war, especially famine and disease. As more efficient methods of inflicting battle casualties have developed, more efficient methods of controlling famine and disease have also developed, so that comparisons among wars in different periods of history become very difficult.

If the birth rate drops during a war—as it generally does—because of the disruption of families, the deficit in births should be counted as part of the population loss due to the war. But the birth rates may rise to abnormal heights immediately after the war, and thus make up in some degree for the deficit.

Certainly the period from 1650 to 1950, when mankind showed such a spectacular rate of growth, could hardly be called a period of peace. If the recurring wars have slowed population growth at all, they have clearly not slowed it effectively.

But whether or not war has been effective in slowing population growth, has population growth been a cause of war? In the case of modern wars, I can see no direct connection. Mussolini and Hitler could shout about the need for room for their people, but at the same time they were making every effort to increase the numbers of their people. Countries like India, China and Java, with the greatest pressures of population, have been among the least warlike of modern peoples. China, currently, seems to have taken to war—but because of ideas rather than because of population pressure. Where population has been alleged as a cause of modern war, it seems to be as a rationalization rather than as a reason. Wars, it seems, are made in the minds of men, not created by forces of nature or economics or population dynamics. Men may have controlled their numbers in the Pleistocene by bashing in each other's skulls, but this too was a cultural phenomenon, and there must be a cultural escape.

CHAPTER *10* FAMINE

I am mourning on my high throne for the vast misfortune, because the Nile flood in my time has not come for seven years! Light is the grain; there is lack of crops and of all kinds of food. Each man has become a thief to his neighbor. They desire to hasten and cannot walk. The child cries, the youth creeps along, and the old man; their souls are bowed down, their legs are bent together and drag along the ground, and their hands rest in their bosoms. The counsel of the great ones in the court is but emptiness. Torn open are the chests of provisions, but instead of contents there is air. Everything is exhausted.—(Inscription on tomb on the Island of Sahal in the first cataract of the Nile, probably from time of Tcheser.)

History, from Tcheser on, is about as full of famines as it is of wars. The famines get less attention than the wars in the history books, but their effect on human population may have been

142

just as great, or greater. War and famine are often so entangled as to be hardly separable, but the war-caused famines, resulting from the disorganization of distribution and the disruption of ordinary farming routines, are still a rather special case. In general, famines result from crop failure, and while crop failure may have political causes, the causes more often are to be found in the vicissitudes of climate—droughts, floods or unseasonable cold.

Famine, then, is characteristically a phenomenon of an agricultural people with a population close to the maximum number that can be supported by the usual harvests. Failure of these harvests thus may be disastrous. In such a situation we would expect, according to the Malthusian propositions, a chronic misery and malnutrition as the population pressed against its food supply even in times of normal harvests. These Malthusian conditions have long applied in areas like India and China, where both chronic malnutrition and epidemic starvation are notorious.

The population effects on chronic malnutrition, among people living close to the limits of available food, are difficult to assess. Statistics of all sorts for such a population are scarce and uncertain. Even if accurate figures were available, "starvation" might not appear as a major cause of death. The effect would rather be indirect, through increased susceptibility to disease. Only with epidemic famine does starvation come to figure directly, but then the mortality may be startlingly great.

A study of the famines of China has shown that between 108 B.C. and A.D. 1911, there were 1,828 famines, or one nearly every year in some part of that vast and teeming land. There is considerable information about some of these famines. The worst in modern times was caused by a great drought in the years 1876 to 1879. "The area affected was 300,000 square miles (about the area of New England, the Middle Atlantic States, Ohio, Indiana and Illinois), and somewhere between 9,000,000 and 13,000,000 people perished from hunger and the disease and violence accompanying prolonged want." Again, in 1920 and 1921, "not less than 20,000,000 people were made destitute by crop failures, and in spite of the most efficient famine relief ever known in China, by which more than 7,000,000 people were fed, at least 500,000 died of want." (Quoting from Warren Thompson, *Population Problems*.)

Famine is far from an exclusively Oriental phenomenon. There are records of 201 famines in the British Islands between A.D. 10 and 1846, when existence in those Islands tended to accord with the Malthusian propositions. The contemporary West has escaped famine except for the special conditions of war; but the contemporary West seems also to have (temporarily?) escaped the Malthusian propositions. The closing date for the list of British famines, 1846, is the date of the great famine of Ireland. This is probably the most carefully studied and fully documented of all historic famines. It also makes a valuable case study from the point of view of general population behavior.

The Irish famine, of course, turns on the potato. How and when the potato got to Ireland is one of those historical mysteries. It is a crop of the Andean region of South America which was not cultivated in North America, Central America or the West Indies in pre-Columbian times; and it attracted relatively little attention from the early Spanish explorers. It was introduced into Spain at least as early as 1570, and by 1588 it was an established garden vegetable in various parts of Spain and Italy. One theory is that the potato got to Ireland by way of a shipwreck after the defeat of the Armada (1588). The first definite reference to the potato in Ireland is in a manuscript about the household arrangements of Lady Montgomery in the year 1606; among the inducements she offered to men working on her estates were "a garden plot to live on and some land for flax and potatoes."

However it got there, the potato soon became an important part of the Irish environment. How rapidly it became the basic food of the Irish people is not entirely clear. One authority considers that this was true as early as 1630; but other scholars consider that its adoption was considerably slower. Certainly, however, the Irish population had become completely dependent on this single crop by the end of the eighteenth century, so that crop failure in 1845 could become a gigantic disaster.

Dr. Redcliffe Salaman, who has written a fascinating book on the history of the potato, devotes several chapters to an examination of this problem of the adoption of the potato in Ireland. Human beings are very conservative in their food habits, and great changes in diet have generally been slow indeed; yet here, within the space of perhaps a hundred years, a whole country became completely dependent on an entirely new crop.

Like most aspects of history, this episode of the Irish and the potato turns out to be a complex affair in which cause and effect seem to be all tangled up. My impression, after reading Salaman, is that any understanding of this period of Irish history requires about equal attention to relations with the English and to relations with the potato—and even these are not separable, since the adoption of the potato may have been partly a consequence of the activities of the English.

The potato plant, to be sure, turned out to be admirably adapted to the Irish climate and soil, but people don't adopt new foods just because they grow easily. Dr. Salaman shows that the explanation lies in politics as much as in climate—that the new crop fitted neatly into a region where the previous cattle economy had been badly disrupted by the wars, revolutions and continuous unrest caused by the English adventures in Ireland.

The spread of the potato in Ireland thus may have been caused, in part, by the circumstances of history; but it also, in turn, had historical effects. In particular, it changed the whole picture of the relations between the population and the food supply. The population of Ireland grew from something like two million in 1687 to 8,175,000 in 1841, a fourfold increase in 150 years (not counting several hundred thousand who emigrated to England or America). A very careful and scholarly investigation of this extraordinary population growth, made by K. H. Connell, concludes that the primary "cause" was the potato.

This Irish population growth is one of the neatest illustrations of the Malthusian theory that a population tends to expand to the limit of its food supply. The evidence, though hazy and indirect, tends to indicate that the population of Ireland remained fairly stable through the middle ages, as did that of England, limited somewhat indirectly by the food supply possible with the nature of the crops and the kind of land tenure. In the medieval world, before a man could marry and raise children, he had to find some means of support, even as a serf, by gaining rights to land for crops or pasturage. The various systems of land tenure, individual and communal, differed greatly in detail, but they tended to stabilize population-subsistence relationships—though, to be sure, at a level that we would find uncomfortable, or miserable.

The civil disturbances of Ireland, the varying laws and policies enforced by the English in their attempts to subjugate and exploit the country, and the advent of the potato, all combined to break down whatever "balance" the Irish population had maintained during the medieval period. The Irishman, like everybody else, was probably always inclined to marry early; with the breakdown of the old social structure and the easy availability of potato subsistence, there was nothing to stop him from indulging in this inclination. All he needed was an acre of land which, planted to potatoes, would support a family of five through the year, according to a contemporary estimate. A sod hut for living quarters was easily built in a few days with the help of neighbors and friends—the value of such a hut, according to another contemporary account, would be about 30 shillings! Children, instead of a liability, were a help from an early age in tending the potato patch. So everything combined to allow the Irish to embark upon a spectacular spree of reproducing themselves.

The first regular census, of 1821, showed a population of 6,802,000; the census of 1831, 7,767,000; the census of 1841, 8,175,000. There were local crop failures, there were all sorts of internal and external political troubles, and the poverty and miserable living conditions of the Irish peasant became notorious in a world where poverty and misery were common everywhere. Yet the breeding spree, supported by the miraculous potato, continued.

Disaster appeared in 1845 in a form of a disease, the potato blight, new to Europe, which immediately became epidemic everywhere that potatoes were grown on the continent. Dr. Salaman writes:

The disease attacked without warning the growing plants, destroying in a few days, fields of potatoes which till then had been proudly resplendent in all their pomp of dark green leaf and purple bloom, leaving nothing but black and withered stalks. Nor were its ravages halted by the death of the tops: before the peasants had time to harvest the crop, the tubers were found to be stained and beginning to rot. Those who had gathered their crop and placed them in the clamps, found them rotten and useless within a few weeks.

There were many theories about the cause of the disease: that it was due to volcanic action within the earth, that it was a "gangrene" produced by the aphids, that it was a form of cholera that had spread to the potato, that it was an act of God to punish the lazy and sinful Irish. The British government tried a variety of relief measures, but there were many who thought this interference with the ways of Providence unwise, and that the Irish should be left to starve. The point of view was expressed by Alfred Smee, one of the leading surgeons of his day:

This effect of depending too exclusively on the culture of the Potato is fearfully exhibited in the Irish people where the potato has begotten millions of paupers who live but are not clothed, who marry but do not work, caring for nothing but their dish of potatoes. . . . If left to itself this fearful state of things would have remedied itself: for had the people the control of their own community, and had the potato crop failed to the extent to which it has this year, these people having no relation with any other, would have been left to their own resources, which being destroyed, would have left them without food.

The blight struck again in 1846, and in these two years more than a million people died directly of starvation or of the diseases consequent on famine conditions. Large efforts were made at relief through soup kitchens and government work projects, but no man who owned as much as a half acre of ground was eligible for relief. Many starved rather than abandon their lifeline to the future, but others by this very mechanism of relief were rendered homeless and still greater numbers were forcibly evicted from their homes for failure to pay rent. For these, the only possible way out was emigration, and the great wave of Irish movement to the United States began.

Irish emigration had started before the famine. Connell has estimated that an average of about 4,000 a year emigrated to America between 1780 and 1815, giving a total of something like 140,000; and that about a million Irish emigrated to America between 1815 and 1845. He thinks that some 600,000 moved to England and Scotland during this same period. The census figures for the population of Ireland itself, then, are not a complete measure of the astonishing fertility of these people in the prefamine era.

The movement out of Ireland increased greatly with the onset of the famine: 61,242 persons left in 1845, according to the Irish census; 105,953 in 1846; double that in 1847. There was a good potato crop in 1848 and emigration dropped to 178,000; but in 1849 it rose again to 214,000; and the outward movement continued high all through the century.

The population of Ireland in 1952 (Northern Ireland and the Republic of Ireland) was about 4,300,000, hardly more than half the prefamine population of 1841, and the population has been about this figure for the last fifty years. The actual drop in numbers was a consequence of the emigration, but the continuing stability reflects a basic change in the habits of the people. The marriage pattern has changed, land tenure systems have changed, agriculture has become more diversified and the economy has changed in other ways. The resulting population stability, however, seems to be not so much the consequence of conscious planning and legislation, as of more or less unconscious changes in the Irish culture. It is a situation that would surely warrant detailed sociological study, though I do not know of any such study.

The population-resources adjustment of Ireland may have a high cost in some ways. The lowered population has been achieved primarily through postponement of marriage—through "moral restraint" in the sense of Malthus. Ireland now has about the lowest marriage rate of any European country and one cannot help but wonder whether this is "desirable" or "healthy" from the point of view of the social and psychological well-being of the people.

The Irish story is unique in that the consequence of a famine or series of famines has been the long-term decline of population and the establishment of conditions which make the recurrence of famine unlikely. The repeated famines of the Orient have led to no such population readjustment, no such drastic change in the social habits of the people. There the population continues to live precariously at the limit possible with normal food supply, with resulting catastrophe when normal conditions fail. The Malthusian propositions seem to apply in full force.

The areas of occasional catastrophic famine are also the areas of chronic malnutrition, of dense agricultural populations with high death rates, low standards of living, undeveloped technology, and all of the other classic symptoms of overpopulation. Since the planet has become a neighborhood, the problems of these areas have become problems of concern to everyone, and we have a growing literature on the ways of implementing technological aid to these "backward" and overpopulated countries.

There is every shade in the spectrum of opinion about this population problem, and the most widely different views can be held with great tenacity and defended with ferocity. One of the most interesting theories has been developed by Josué de Castro in a book called *The Geography of Hunger*. The thesis of this book, if I may greatly oversimplify, is that overpopulation is caused by malnutrition. This, at least, is a refreshing reversal of the usual theory, that malnutrition is a result of overpopulation, though I am not persuaded by the logic of de Castro's book.

De Castro deals with the relationship between nutrition and reproduction at what might be called a physiological level; whereas I think that in man the cultural factors overwhelm any likely physiological effects. One may be able to show a relation between diet and litter size in rats, and there may well be a direct relation between the kind of food eaten and fertility in man. But when one examines actual situations, like Ireland, the explanation of changed fertility in man always seems to lie in things like marriage rates, birth control practices, infanticide, or such-like social factors, rather than in relative or absolute amounts of protein or vitamins or other things in the diet.

As far as I can see, most of the evidence from physiological studies indicates that malnutrition and famine tend to reduce fertility in man, so that the high reproductive rates in the Orient persist in spite of malnutrition rather than because of it.

One of the most interesting, and certainly the most thorough, of studies of the effects of starvation on man was carried out by Ancel Keys and a group of collaborators at the University of Minnesota, during World War II, using a group of volunteers from among "conscientious objectors." Their studies were written up and published in two huge volumes, which contain not only the results of their own observations, but also the results of combing through a vast literature.

One of the first effects of starvation on the men in the Minnesota group was a loss of all interest in sex. Their thoughts and dreams turned on food, not women; and their normal pattern of sexual activity, whether of coitus or masturbation, was broken.

The diminution of the strength of the sex drive was so dramatic that the subjects were struck by the change and used colorful language to describe it. As one of them put it, "I have no more sexual feeling than a sick oyster. . . ." In the rehabilitation period, sexual impulses, needs and interests were very slow in regaining their pre-experimental intensity; they were still low at the end of the 12th week of rehabilitation.

Keys made all sorts of physiological measurements on his starvation subjects, including measurements of semen volume and sperm count. From these it appears that the men would probably have been sterile even if they had had the drive and opportunity for sex. Recovery was slow, and the semen did not become normal until more than 20 weeks after rehabilitation had started.

The female reproductive system is surely also affected by starvation. The most direct evidence is the frequency of amenorrhea, or interruption of regular menstruation, under internment camp conditions. Keys quotes one observation, however, of a physician who noted that menstruation continued to be regular among emaciated Chinese women, suggesting an "adaptation to chronic starvation."

Direct evidence on fertility under actual famine conditions is hard to come by, because the conditions that lead to famine are not conducive to orderly statistical studies. Such evidence as there is, however, all tends to indicate greatly lowered fertility. For instance, during the severe famine in Madras in 1877, there were only 39 births in the relief camps, although more than 100,000 people were being cared for over a period of some months. The birth rate dropped early in the famine, probably as a consequence of the preceding near-famine conditions, and continued low for a considerable time. Nine months after the worst food shortage the birth rate was four to five per 1,000, as compared to a usual rate of 29 per 1,000 in the same districts.

Statistical services were maintained in the Netherlands all through World War II, and the record of births there is consequently one of the few available for famine conditions. In Rotterdam, for instance, there was no significant change in the birth rate from 1939 through 1944. Food was moderately restricted from the middle of 1940; but serious failure of food supply did not occur until September, 1944, with a low point in availability of food from January to April, 1945. The birth rate started to fall in July, 1945, ten months after the failure of food the previous September. By October, 1945, births were less than half of normal (averaging 84 per week as compared with 210 to 245 per week in 1944). The birth rate in Rotterdam all through this period thus reflected neatly the food conditions prevailing nine or ten months previously.

Yet the half-starved millions of the Orient continue to reproduce themselves at very high rates. Perhaps there is an adaptation to chronic hunger. Certainly life goes on, even though it may seem to be painful and miserable. But I cannot believe that the reproduction is caused by the hunger; or that the reproduction will slow up just because the hunger is eased. The hunger is, while present, the primary thing to be dealt with; and perhaps under conditions of less stress, when people do not need to think about their hunger, they learn to think more carefully about the future and are thus less apt, blindly and miserably, to reproduce themselves, careless of how these new generations will find the means of subsistence. But this sort of relationship between hunger and ideas is cultural, not physiological.

Conditions of overcrowding, with chronic malnutrition, are also classically the conditions that breed disease—not only the deficiency diseases that clearly result directly from the food situation, but also the infectious diseases. War and famine, dramatic though they may be in human history, are dwarfed by the third major cause of ecological death in man, disease.

CHAPTER *11* DISEASE

Louis Pasteur was probably more responsible than anyone else for the popularization of the idea that germs cause disease. He must have been a dramatic lecturer as well as a clever designer of experiments and demonstrations, and he gave the war on germs a fine start. He worked on tame and helpful germs, too, like the yeasts of fermentation; but the bad germs got the big press, and all of the efforts of bacteriologists since to rehabilitate micro-organisms, by pointing out how essential they are in the economy of nature, have been of little avail.

Perhaps the modern studies of infection should really be dated, not from Pasteur, but from the potato blight of 1846. This epidemic, which was universal in Europe, though catastrophic only in Ireland, stimulated an immense amount of both speculation and careful study. Several scientists, both in England and on the continent, recognized that the disease was caused by

154

a fungus and disseminated by spores. The work was, however, chiefly of theoretical importance, since it did not lead to any dramatic "cures" as did the later studies of infection in man. Yet it did mark the beginnings of an ever-growing interest in the nature of infection.

In the case of the diseases of man, the systematic and large-scale search for the causative micro-organisms and the study of their ways of spread, of the nature of their damage, and of means of preventing or curing the infection, are mostly matters of the last seventy-five or so years of history. The results have become such an integral part of our common knowledge, and the effect on both our ways of thought and ways of living has been so great that it is hard to realize how recent all of this is.

Out of this, too, has gradually come the realization that germs are far from being the only villains in the story of disease. As we failed to find particular bugs causing this malady or that, we have come to recognize whole new categories of disease: nutritional and deficiency diseases, psychosomatic diseases, organic diseases, hereditary diseases.

But the infectious diseases, the diseases caused by some germ or other, continue to get the largest share of medical attention, and surely have been the most important in relation to the vicissitudes of human population. The prevalence of infectious disease has had a tremendous influence on the prevalence of people; and in this chapter I want to look at the biology of infectious disease from this point of view.

There can be little doubt but what infectious disease has been the chief cause of death in man during most of his recent history. This is no longer true in the modern West where medicine has made such dramatic progress in the control of infection, so that death generally is now the direct result of some noninfectious thing like heart disease, cancer or "accident"; and it may not have been true way back in the Old Stone Age when man was much more directly an element in the "natural" community of

the forest and savannah. But through all of the period of complex culture, of civilization, while man flourished and increased
so abundantly, disease was surely the chief agent of destruction,
outrunning war and famine. Indeed, war and famine did not
operate so much directly, as indirectly by favoring disease.

These are sweeping statements, but I doubt whether anyone
will quarrel with them because the importance of disease is accepted as a truism. It would be nice, though, if we could document them, if we could say, surely, what diseases afflicted the
Egyptians or the Greeks or the Mayans or the ancient Chinese,
and assess the relative importance of different diseases among
these different people. But the study of the history of disease is
loaded with difficulties, and there are very few things we can
say with certainty, despite the brilliant detective work that has
gone into its study.

I have a feeling that this great importance of infectious disease
is something that has come to man along with civilization, or at
least along with agriculture and the possibility thus of supporting densely crowded populations. But this "feeling" can be supported only by the most indirect of evidence, and by shaky
deductions from doubtful premises. We really know very little
about the origins of any of our diseases; and new diseases may
be forming right under our noses, but proof would be difficult
to come by.

We have a fine documentation of the increasing importance of
poliomyelitis in recent years. But is this a "new" disease, or an
old disease that is only now becoming commonly recognized, or
an old disease that is changing its appearance because of changes
in human habits? The same sort of question may be asked
about a whole family of diseases called the "encephalitides" or,
in a slightly changed form, of the influenza that swept the world
at the close of World War I. And there are similar questions
about the puzzling sudden notoriety of syphilis in Europe at the
beginning of the sixteenth century.

The converse of the problem of new diseases is that of old diseases that have disappeared. Sometimes we are sure what the disease was. The Black Death of medieval Europe, for instance, was the bubonic plague that smolders in many parts of the world today and breaks out occasionally in epidemic form. It appeared with dramatic suddenness in central Europe in 1348, when it is estimated that a quarter of the population were killed. Successive epidemics in 1361, 1371 and 1382 were calamitous enough, but successively less severe. Plague persisted locally, and in restricted epidemics, during the fifteenth and sixteenth centuries; and then broke out again in the great plagues of 1663 to 1668, including the London plague of 1664. Then plague gradually disappeared, not appearing in Europe in epidemic form after 1800. Why? I think no one can be sure of the answer. Isolated cases have appeared often enough, but no epidemic sweep has started; though in the eighteenth and early nineteenth centuries, knowledge of how to control an epidemic was no better than it had been in the seventeenth century.

The history of leprosy in Europe is another mystery. It apparently was a common disease in Europe in the middle ages, judging from the number of leprosaria and frequency of reference to the disease. But after the middle of the fifteenth century, it began to decline, and by the seventeenth century it had practically disappeared from Europe. Again there is no clear explanation. Possible improvement in sanitary conditions, treatment, or economic changes seem hardly adequate explanations. One trouble, of course, is that we still have no thorough knowledge of the epidemiology of this disease.

Leprosy and plague are diseases with long and continuous histories in the Orient; and their rise and decline in Europe can be looked at as a problem in the geography of disease; though it remains equally inexplicable whether considered as geography or history. There are some diseases, however, that are purely historical, that seem to have disappeared completely. One of

these is the "English sweating sickness," described by Hans
Zinsser in his delightful book on *Rats, Lice and History*.

The disease began without warning, usually at night or toward
morning, with a chill and with tremors. Soon there was fever, and
profound weakness. Accompanying this were cardiac pains and
palpitation, in some cases vomiting, severe headache, and stupor,
but rarely delirium. . . . The profuse sweating, which was the most
notable characteristic, began soon after the onset of the fever.
Death came with astonishing speed. It is stated that many cases
died within a day, and some even within a few hours.

This sweating sickness first turns up in history in 1485, in
the army of Henry VII, after the battle of Bosworth, spreading
over England rapidly from east to west. "In London it killed,
within the first week, two Lord Mayors and six Aldermen."
There was a second epidemic in 1507, much like the first; and a
third in 1518. In 1529 there occurred the most severe epidemic
of all, which swept over much of Europe. "It reached Vienna
during the siege of the city by the Sultan Soliman and, probably
ravaging the Turkish army, may have had some effect on the
raising of the siege." The fifth and last epidemic occurred in
1551. Since then no epidemic disease with these symptoms has
appeared, and it is impossible to identify the sweating disease
with anything that we know.

So we have diseases that are apparently "new" in modern
times, diseases that have changed greatly in geographical pattern, and diseases that have disappeared—without deliberate
interference from man, without benefit of science or medicine.
In fact, the pattern of disease, as we look back over history,
seems constantly to have been changing. The relation between
disease and mortality, the effect of disease on human populations, has thus never been a constant or easily calculable factor.
When we try to figure out the role of disease in the history of
human populations, we are thus on uncertain ground.

Infectious disease is a special form of the parasitic relationship so common among organisms. And parasitism itself, on examination, turns out to be difficult to define, to set off as a special kind of relationship. Animals and plants have all sorts of ways of living off each other and with each other. Biologists use many words, like parasitism, predation, symbiosis and saprophytism, to label such relationships, but the distinctions have a tendency to blur, and the student is apt to end up completely confused, particularly if he is enamored of nice, precise definitions for the words he uses.

For our present purposes, we can probably get along well enough with the general idea of parasitism, of some small organism living at the expense of a big organism, usually inside it, and not being of any direct help to the big organism, the host. If the parasite causes obvious harm, it is causing "disease"; and there can be every gradation in the amount of harm, in the severity of the disease.

A considerable variety of parasites are capable of causing disease in man—bacteria, viruses, protozoa, parasitic worms of several kinds, and a few parasitic fungi. Diseases with quite similar symptoms, be they fever, rash, cough, diarrhea, or what not, may be caused by quite different parasites; and the identification of the parasite, the precise diagnosis of the disease, may thus require elaborate laboratory study. The disease itself, the impairment of health, is the end result of many sorts of factors affecting the host, the parasite, and the environment in which the host-parasite relation occurs. This all adds up to make epidemiology, the study of the natural history of disease, a complex subject.

There are many different ways in which we can group diseases, depending on the point of view from which we are studying them. They are most commonly classified either according to the kind of parasite causing the disease, or according to the organ system of the human body primarily affected (respiratory, urogenital, digestive and so forth). But from the point of view of disease and population, one of the most interesting things is the way of spread: whether direct, from man to man, or indirect, by means of vectors or alternate hosts.

In the case of contagious diseases, like measles, smallpox, and mumps, the parasite can pass directly from one host to another. This, at first sight, seems the most sensible procedure from the point of view of the parasite, and one wonders why parasites have developed so many complicated and indirect ways of getting from one host to another, by way of mosquitoes or snails or fleas, or waiting encysted in the muscles of a pig for months or years.

One answer, I think, lies in population density. If the parasite is to pass directly from man to man, men must frequently come in direct contact. This happens under conditions of civilization, where men by the thousands live in crowded cities, and where there is frequent contact among cities through trade, travel and war. But conditions are very different with men organized into the small bands of a food-gathering culture, which must have been the circumstance for most of human history.

The difficulty is particularly apparent in the case of an acute, self-limiting infection, such as measles, smallpox or mumps. The parasite gets established in a new host and multiplies enormously for a week or two; but protective mechanisms start to operate in the host, producing biochemical conditions that kill the parasite (if the host isn't killed first). The parasite is out of luck in either case, unless it can manage to get a new host. With many of these diseases, host immunity is permanent, so that a particular host that has survived infection can never be infected by the same kind of parasite again. There must, then, be a constant supply of new hosts readily available.

These conditions are present over much of the modern world, and they have been present in the Mediterranean, the Near East and parts of the Far East and Orient for some thousands of years now. But they were not present before the Neolithic revolution, before the development of agriculture and cities, and I wonder whether these contagious diseases may not largely be post-Neolithic developments.

This is the more possible because a good many of these self-limited contagions are caused by viruses. Viruses are very queer things. They have been subjected to intensive study in recent years, but we still don't know too much about them. They are submicroscopic particles, too small to be studied with a microscope; and the ones that we know are all obligate parasites, living in the cells of other organisms. They are recognizable then chiefly by the damage they cause, or by chemical changes associated with their presence, and much of our knowledge of them is indirect.

We keep finding more and more different kinds of viruses that can infect man. Some of these cause very mild diseases and have been discovered more or less by accident. Yellow fever is caused by a virus, and since this is a terrible and important disease, scientists have studied it in many parts of the tropics. They have also stumbled upon a whole series of other viruses in the course of trying to isolate yellow fever virus, or of making surveys of immunity to yellow fever. Some of these other viruses still are known only in the laboratory, but in other cases they have been found to be associated with some mild, hardly noticed disease of local populations.

Again, there seems to be a whole series of viruses associated with "colds" and influenza-like diseases of man. Some of these leave only a temporary immunity, the sort of thing we are all familiar with in the case of colds. These viruses have been difficult to study because, for the most part, it has been impossible to transmit them from man to laboratory animals where they can be experimented with.

There are, then, a remarkable number of different sorts of viruses associated with man. Some of them cause contagious diseases with temporary immunity, like the "common cold"; some cause contagious diseases with long-term immunity, like measles; some of them are transmissible only indirectly, like yellow fever through certain mosquitoes; some cause very mild diseases; others, diseases with high fatality rates; some of them may normally cause subclinical infections hardly noticeable, like polio growing in the intestine, with occasional disastrous effects, as when polio virus gets into the nervous system.

With some of these viruses, we have managed to get infections in laboratory animals, so that the virus can be studied over long periods of time under controlled conditions. Sometimes, under these conditions, we get remarkable changes. The virus can gradually get "adapted" to a new kind of animal, or to a new kind of tissue within the animal; or it may increase in virulence, or decrease in virulence.

Yellow fever virus illustrates this nicely. For a long time, it was thought that this virus could infect only man, and the famous experiments of Walter Reed and his colleagues demonstrating mosquito transmission were made with human volunteers. In 1927, a group of scientists working in Africa found that the rhesus monkey could be infected and the virus could then be studied under controlled laboratory conditions. Three years later, Max Theiler, working at the Harvard Medical School in Boston, found he could infect white mice by injecting virus directly into their brains and that the virus changed, after a few brain passages, so that it grew rapidly in brain tissue, causing a fatal paralytic disease in the mice and becoming less often fatal when injected into the monkeys. He and others then tried growing this changed virus in chicken embryos from which the brain had been removed, to see what would happen. They kept testing it for virulence by injecting virus at each passage into monkey brains; and suddenly, from one passage to another, the virus changed, so that it no longer killed the monkey even when injected directly into the brain. The monkey that had been injected with this harmless virus, however, was forever immune to the ordinary virus—he had had a harmless kind of yellow fever that protected him against the fatal variety. A yellow fever vaccine had been discovered.

Now if such dramatic changes can occur in the laboratory, they can also occur in nature. In nature, yellow fever virus would not be likely to get from a monkey to the inside of a chicken egg; but the viruses are constantly getting into new hosts and new situations where, for the most part, they die; but where occasionally they may adapt. And the adaptation may well result in a "new" disease.

We don't, then, necessarily have to assume that all of our diseases have always been with us. And there is the further, terrifying possibility, that new and highly fatal diseases may come upon us at any moment. George Stewart used this possibility for depopulating the world in his novel, *The Earth Abides*. It is more fashionable now for novelists to depopulate the world through atomic explosions—and it is perhaps more probable that this will be our fate. But germ warfare, presumably, is also not being overlooked; and if viruses can be tamed in the laboratory, perhaps also they can be deliberately molded into more potent agents of destruction. The problem of how to train a germ to distinguish one nationality from another is insurmountable, and this may hold up germ warfare, though the probability of self-destruction seems no deterrent in the mad career of weapons development.

When we turn from the contagious diseases to the diseases that are caused by parasites with indirect ways of getting from host to host, we find a different sort of a situation. It is unlikely that such diseases are "new" even in a geological sense. The complex adjustments between parasite and alternate hosts and environmental circumstances are the sort of thing that must have been slow in developing. Interestingly enough, none of these diseases is at present a serious problem in Europe or North

America, though they have been important in the not-too-distant past, and continue important in the areas we call "backward."

Malaria is one of these indirectly transmitted diseases: the most important of them, and the most thoroughly studied. Until very recently, it was generally considered the most important of all human diseases in terms of both cost in deaths and cost in economic loss through illness and lowered efficiency. It may no longer hold this position since the use of DDT as an insecticide has made control cheap enough for almost any community to afford.

The parasites causing malaria are protozoans of the genus Plasmodium, microscopic animals that live within the red blood cells of their vertebrate hosts. Four species of Plasmodium are known to infect man, and the resulting diseases have somewhat different symptoms, especially in the periodicity of the fevers (hence the names "tertian" and "quartan" malaria). These plasmodia are "host specific"—they will infect only man. But several other species of plasmodia are known from various monkeys and apes, which makes it seem likely that the plasmodia have been associated with the primates through much of their evolution. Plasmodia of different sorts are also known from many kinds of birds, reptiles, and a few bats and other mammals.

The human plasmodia and some, at least, of the monkey plasmodia, are transmitted by mosquitoes of the genus Anopheles. The bird plasmodia are transmitted by quite different mosquitoes. The transmission is not a simple process of the mosquito picking up the germs in one blood meal and carrying them around to inject into the next person bitten; it involves, rather, complex adaptations on the part of the parasite. The ordinary parasite, growing in the blood of man, dies promptly in the mosquito stomach. But from time to time, special forms of the parasite appear in the blood. These, if picked up by a mosquito, burst out of the blood cells in the mosquito stomach and turn out to include two kinds: small "male" parasites (microgametes), eight or more wriggling out of a single blood cell; and large "female" (macrogametes) which are fertilized in the mosquito stomach by the microgametes.

This fertilized female plasmodium edges through the cells of the stomach wall of the mosquito and forms a cyst which grows and eventually bursts to release hundreds of "sporozoites" into the body cavity of the mosquito. These work their way through the body of the mosquito to land, eventually, in the large salivary glands of the insect. They can live there indefinitely, as long as the mosquito lives; and each time the mosquito bites, some of them are forced out, along with the salivary secretions, into the blood of the animal being bitten. If the animal happens to be a man, the parasites presently lodge in the liver, go through some transformations there, and then start infecting the red blood cells, completing the cycle.

As far as we can tell, the parasite does not harm the mosquito: mosquitoes infected with plasmodia and uninfected mosquitoes will, on the average, have exactly the same length of life in the laboratory. It has always seemed to me, though, that these growing cysts (and there may be dozens of them in one insect) must at least give the mosquito something corresponding to a stomach-ache. The failure of the parasite to cause apparent harm to the mosquito has led some scientists to believe that the mosquito must be the original host, on the theory that the older the host-parasite association, the less harm the parasite is liable to cause. I have never put much stock in this theory since the parasite has probably been associated with both the mosquitoes and man or man's ancestors for several million years.

If you add up all of the things that have to happen, it would seem unlikely that the malaria parasite would ever get from one man to another—yet millions of new infections occur every year. (It's like the fertilization of the human egg, which also seems to me improbable, and yet happens all the time.) In the case of malaria, the right kind of a mosquito has to bite a man at the time when sexual parasites are in his blood (when you try to infect mosquitoes on a man, you sometimes have a hard time); the mosquito has to live for at least ten days after biting for the parasite cycle to be completed (and the hazards of life for a mosquito are immense; the average life span as an adult is probably only three or four days); and the mosquito must then bite a susceptible man (not a cow or a bird or a man who already has that kind of malaria).

The complications of this transmission mechanism explain much of the history and geography of malaria. I suspect that the original home of both man and malaria is tropical Africa, and there, where all conditions are favorable—human hosts fairly abundant, anopheline mosquitoes abundant and with habits that lead to close association with man, and climate favorable for the survival of mosquitoes and the development of the parasites—the disease has probably always been endemic. Man and the disease arrive at a sort of balance. Most humans become infected in infancy or childhood and build up a tolerance for the local strains of parasites. The disease surely causes an appreciable loss in human energy, but the loss is far less dramatic than in epidemic situations.

Malaria has a long history in the Mediterranean. It was clearly described by Hippocrates (400 B.C.), and there are frequent references to intermittent fevers by ancient Roman writers. The Roman Campagna has been a very unhealthy place to live during many periods of history because of malaria, and there is a nice correlation between the upswings of malaria and the downswings of Roman prosperity.

The mosquitoes of the Mediterranean region are not nearly as good vectors of malaria as are those of tropical Africa, and this probably accounts for the fact that malaria has had great ups and downs in the Mediterranean while it seems to have remained a constant and steady factor in tropical Africa. Several of the commonest Mediterranean anophelines will bite man only when nothing else is available. I once demonstrated this in Albania by spending the night in a large cage with about a thousand anophelines of one of these species, along with a small calf. I didn't get bitten by a single mosquito—they all preferred the calf. The Mediterranean habit of living with the livestock thus may well offer considerable protection against malaria, and the ratio of cattle to men at different times and in different places may have considerable effect on the prevalence of malaria. The disappearance of malaria from Denmark in the last century may have been a result of the development of the dairy industry there, though malaria has generally been retreating both in Europe and North America during the last hundred years. The retreat started long before the transmission of the disease was understood, and thus before direct public health measures could be considered responsible.

The relations between disease and population density are thus of different sorts. With an immunity-producing contagious disease, such as smallpox, the continuing existence of the disease requires a large population in frequent contact; and with such diseases, in general, the larger the population, the more likely the persistence of the disease. In such cases, the disease is "endemic," always present, with most everyone acquiring the disease at an early age.

Where a contagion is not constantly maintained within a population, large numbers of people may grow up without immunity; and the contagion, once introduced, may sweep through the population as an epidemic. Some contagions seem almost everywhere to spread only periodically, as epidemics; while others have foci where they persist in endemic form under particularly favorable conditions, to break out periodically as epidemics in other parts of the world.

Where transmission is indirect, or involves vectors or alternate hosts, the relation between the disease and population density is more complex. Malaria, for instance, can rarely maintain itself in the centers of large cities because, while people are numerous enough, the vector mosquitoes do not breed in urban situations. It is most commonly a disease of villages and the fringes of cities, where marshes, ponds or streams provide suitable breeding places for the mosquitoes. Plague, on the other hand, dependent on rats and fleas, may be most severe in unsanitary cities.

It would be difficult to overestimate the importance of changes in the geography of disease over the globe since about 1400, for it has been associated with the modern movements of people in exploration or settlement. Both the contagions and the vector-transmitted diseases are involved.

The vector-transmitted diseases are, in general, more chained by geography than the contagions, because of their complex life-histories. But the parasite of malaria, for instance, can be transmitted by almost any species of anopheline mosquito; and there are several hundred different kinds of anopheline mosquitoes, and one or another of them occurs in almost every part of the world. The parasite thus often finds favorable conditions in quite new situations. It seems to me most probable that malaria was first brought to America by the Spaniards, and that yellow fever came over with some of the early African slaves. In the case of malaria, American mosquitoes proved excellent vectors; in the case of yellow fever, the vector was brought in with the disease—a mosquito that bred in the water tanks of the ships.

The most dramatic effects, however, were caused by the contagions which move easily with new contacts among populations; and of these contagions, smallpox has probably been the most important from the population point of view. It seems quite reasonable, in fact, to consider smallpox as the most effective agent in the Spanish conquest of America. We get only glimpses of it in the chronicles, but these make it clear enough that the smallpox arrived with the Spaniards and, in the campaigns of conquest, generally spread through the population ahead of them. As one missionary noted, "the Indians die so easily that the bare look and smell of a Spaniard causes them to give up the ghost."

All accounts agree that the island of Hispaniola was teeming with people when Columbus first landed there. Plausible estimates for the population go as high as a million, and we are fairly safe in assuming that there were at least several hundred thousand aboriginal inhabitants. But they became extinct in a remarkably short time after the intrusion of a few hundreds of Spaniards. The histories mostly explain this on the basis of the cruelty of the Spaniards on the one hand, and the lack of stamina of the Indians on the other. But the gunpowder and ferocity of the Spaniards, however potent, seem completely inadequate to explain the events without the addition of a few new viruses and bacteria.

Smallpox clearly was with Cortez in his conquest of Mexico. As the Stearns tell the story in their study of *The Effect of Smallpox on the Amerindian:*

At the time of the departure of Narvaez from Cuba in order to join Cortez, smallpox was raging there severely. A pioneer vessel of the fleet brought the disease to Cozumel, whence it spread to the continent. . . . After desolating the coast regions, the disease crossed the plateau region and in the summer broke out around the lakes in passing to the land along the "western sea." For sixty days it raged with such virulence that the period of the raging of "hueyzahuatl," or great pest, fixed itself as a central point in the chronology of the natives. In most districts half the population died, towns became deserted, and those who recovered presented an appearance which horrified their neighbors. . . . In December, 1520, Cortez, on his way to Montezuma and the capital city of Mexico, stopped at Cholula, where he was asked to nominate new

Indian chiefs to replace those dead from smallpox. Cuitlahuatzin, the younger brother of Montezuma, who had tried to rectify his elder brother's blunders, died of smallpox after a reign of three months. King Totoquihuatzin of Tlacopan was also an early victim of the disease.

We have, of course, no nice statistics on the mortality rates of smallpox among the American Indians. One can only guess that it killed a respectable proportion of the population. When the disease appeared for the first time in Iceland, in 1707, it was said to have killed 18,000 out of a population of 50,000; and what evidence there is indicates that the mortality rates among some of the Indian epidemics were much higher than this.

There is ample evidence of the havoc caused by smallpox among the North American Indians—and here the Europeans sometimes, at least, appreciated their advantage. There seems to be no question about the occasional use of smallpox in a sort of "germ warfare." Sir Jeffrey Amherst, a British commander facing an Indian revolt, was explicit: "You will do well to try to inoculate the Indians by means of blankets as well as to try every other method that can serve to extirpate this execrable race." A Captain Ecuyer of the Royal Americans noted that "out of regard" for two Indian chiefs, "we have given them two blankets and a handkerchief out of the smallpox hospital. I hope it will have the desired effect."

Smallpox may have been the most important ally of the Europeans in the depopulation of America, but it surely was not the only one. Among the islands of the Pacific where contacts were made later, and where more reliable accounts of the effects of new diseases are available, measles and mumps were prime agents of mortality, along with smallpox, tuberculosis, and various intestinal and respiratory diseases apparently new to the people. Venereal disease, which has generally been one of the "blessings" brought by Europeans to isolated peoples, has also had important population effects through reducing fertility, if not as a direct cause of mortality.

It seems to me that in tropical Africa we have had a nice reversal of this picture of the spread of disease through Western contact. Here the indigenous people were, for a long time, protected from Europeans by their diseases—yellow fever, potent local strains of malaria, and special diseases like sleeping-sickness. Of course, tropical Africa had had an indirect contact with the civilizations of the Mediterranean and the Near East for a very long time, and it may be that the special diseases of civilization spread to them at an early period, well ahead of the explorers and colonizers, so that the population had a chance to adapt to the disease situation. It also looks as though Africa, possibly the main focus of much of human evolution, may also have seen the evolution of many of the human diseases, which again would give the long-exposed indigenous population the advantage.

The present pattern of disease in the world, then, in many ways seems to be a consequence of the pattern of exploration, conquest and trade of the modern West. Contagious diseases in particular have tended to become cosmopolitan, and we now have a situation where an epidemic, like that of influenza in 1918, can sweep over the entire globe in a remarkably short time. Shared diseases seem to be one of the consequences of living on a planet that has become a neighborhood.

However unfortunate this has been in the past, there seems no reason it should continue so, because we can share knowledge of the diseases too. Surely, however one measures the accomplishments of Western civilization, one of its greatest achievements has been the understanding and control of infectious disease. So far this knowledge has been applied most effectively within the Western area itself, where the habits of the people and the economics of the situation permit great attention to public and private health. The knowledge is not as contagious as the diseases, and the knowledge itself is often useless in the face of economic handicaps that seem insuperable. But infectious disease surely can be controlled, not only in the West, but everywhere, so that the prime causes of death will be physiological instead of ecological.

We have made no progress toward abolishing death; but by controlling the ecological causes, we have postponed it. This postponement of death, this triumph of medicine and science, has been well enough publicized, but we may as well review it again in the following chapter.

CHAPTER *12* THE POSTPONEMENT OF DEATH

Ponce de Leon could look hopefully for the magic fountain whose waters would keep him forever young. The Marquis de Condorcet, looking at the power that man was beginning to find through scientific ways of thinking, could imagine that medicine would lead eventually to an indefinite prolongation of life. And we can perhaps still imagine this, though neither magic nor science has so far given us any power to prolong the maximum length of human life.

Our success has been in the control of premature death, particularly through the prevention and cure of infectious disease. The success is well enough documented in most Western countries, and can be expressed as a gradual decrease in the number of people per thousand population who die every year, or as an increase in the expectation of life at birth, or as an increase in the average age at which people die—a postponement of death.

The best statistics are for the nineteenth and twentieth cen-

173

turies, but the change seems to have started before that, really antedating the development of medical science. Thus in 1681-1690 in the city of London, there were on the average 42 deaths per thousand population per year; by 1746-1755, this had dropped to 35 deaths per thousand; by 1846-1855, to 25 per thousand. In 1947, the London death rate was 13 per thousand.

Health itself, of course, is not a modern invention, nor is the maintenance of health necessarily directly dependent on contemporary scientific knowledge. The Greeks were much preoccupied with health, and worked out regimes for diet and exercise, and the Romans carried on the idea, as expressed in the slogan: "A sound mind in a sound body." That public health also is an ancient concept is shown by the attention given to aqueducts and baths in classical cities.

Several writings on health survive among the Hippocratic documents, with detailed instructions on food, evacuation, exercise, sleep and the like.

The cultivation of health begins with the moment a man wakes up . . . a young or middle-aged individual should soon before sunrise take a walk of about 10 stadia, in the summer however of only 5, and older men will take a shorter walk in winter as well as in summer. . . . One shall rub the gums in order to strengthen the teeth. . . . The chief meal is to be taken when the body is empty and does not contain any badly digested residue of food. Dinner should be taken in summer soon before sunset and consist of bread, vegetables and barley cake. . . . It is not good for anybody to sleep on the back.

These excerpts are from Henry Sigerist's translation from Diocles. As Sigerist goes on to remark, "It was perfectly obvious that very few people could afford to lead such a life. It was a regime for the wealthy few, for a small upper class leading a life of leisure, a class produced and supported by an economy in which all manual labor was performed by slaves." There were no rules of hygiene for these slaves.

This cult of health had its detractors. Among them was Plato, who thought that perpetual care for health was just another disease. He argued, in the *Republic,* that no one has time to be sick all of his life, on the pretense of attending to his health.

We have no direct vital statistics from ancient Greece, but modern scholars have exercised considerable ingenuity in trying to reconstruct conditions by studying things like skeletal materials and epitaphs in ancient cemeteries. Lawrence Angel, after studying a series of several hundred skeletons from Greek cemeteries of different periods, concluded that "a small but definite increase in length of life accompanied the rise of civilization in ancient Greece." He also found that "some improvement in general health accompanied the increase in length of life between prehistoric and historic times. The skeletal material shows an increase in body size, a probable reduction in arthritis, and a probable improvement in teeth." His comparison of skeletal material from different periods suggested an increase of at least four or five years in life expectancy at any age period. "Probably the actual changes in old age, childhood, and especially infancy were much greater."

Angel is very scientific and conservative about drawing conclusions from his data, but his figures suggest that the average age at death may have shifted from somewhere around 30 in the early Bronze Age, to somewhere around 40 in the classical period. It seems likely, at any rate, that life expectancy in classical Greece reached a high that was not attained again until late medieval times in Europe. And the standards and practice of medicine show a similar history.

Medicine in ancient Greece may have affected only the fortunate few, but it was rational and based on careful observation. In this respect it stands out as a bright exception in the long history of man's attempts to understand and control disease.

Even in ancient Greece, along with the Hippocratic approach to the study of disease as a natural phenomenon, we have what might be called the religious approach to disease, as represented by the cult of Asklepios. And with the fading of the Hellenic spirit in the Mediterranean world, this religious approach came to dominate entirely; and cures became the function first of various heathen cults, and then of the diverse saints and their shrines. The emergence of modern medicine out of this medieval world is a long and complex story, often enough told.

Any attempt to contrast the rational and the religious approach to medicine—or, in equally loaded words, the scientific and the magical approach—is, of course, a gross oversimplification. When we start to trace the origins and development of medicine, we find ourselves caught in the whole tangle of human history with threads leading into the most diverse sorts of human activities. We can't look very closely at this within the frame of the present book, but the subject has considerable relevance insofar as we are trying to gain some understanding of the relation between medicine and health, and health and the behavior of human populations.

There is a curious mixture of the practical and the magical throughout the history of man's relationship with disease. Methods of dealing with wounds, fractures and such-like physical damage have generally tended to be practical; and there is evidence of surgical skill in the bones that survive from the earliest civilizations. Infectious disease, on the other hand, with its mysterious onset and with the equally mysterious end in recovery or death, has tended to look like some sort of supernatural intervention in human affairs and thus has generally been the concern of the priesthood both in ancient civilizations and among contemporary "primitives."

The contrast between the practical craftsmanship of the surgeon-barbers and the philosophical preoccupations of the physician-priests is certainly helpful in understanding many aspects of medical history. In these terms, the emergence of medicine as a science can be regarded as a fusion of the two previously separate developments, as the same person becomes concerned with craftsmanship and philosophy. This then becomes a sort of special case of the general theory that modern science is a result of the union of the worker and the thinker in the same person. The delay in the development of medicine—or science—would then be blamed on the scorn of the thinker for the worker that has prevailed over so much of history and in so many cultures.

It's probably all too simple again. The physician-priests certainly seem foolish to us, with their preoccupation with exorcisms and divinations and theories about spirits and stars and the phases of the moon. But priestly medicine picked up a lot of fairly practical stuff, too, about ways of dealing with disease; and it was dealing in part with the complex relations between body and mind that we still seem only on the verge of understanding. It is tempting to wonder whether our psychotherapists are not still carrying on the legitimate functions of these physician-priests.

And all along there is a third development that gets left out of account in this contrast—the development that might be called folk medicine. Our ancestors had half a million years or so to explore the possible uses of the plants and animals in their environment, and over this stretch of time they did a remarkably thorough job. We'll probably never know how they discovered the drugs, poisons and foods that they so generally use. Often the drugs and remedies of folk medicine seem useless, sometimes clearly harmful; but often, too, they are effective, and folk medicine has contributed much to our modern pharmacopoeia.

I suppose, with all of this, I am trying to say that the origins of modern medicine—or science—are not simple, and that the relationship between medicine and health is not necessarily a direct, one-to-one affair. When we start trying to reconstruct medieval and modern European history, medicine and health, for quite long stretches of time, seem to have no relation to one another. Addison, writing in the *Spectator* of 1711, could maintain that they were antagonistic. "If, we look into the profession of physick, we shall find a most formidable body of men; the sight of them is enough to make a man serious; for we may lay it down as a maxim, that when a nation abounds in physicians, it grows thin of people."

Indeed, it is probably safe to say that the direct effect of medical developments on the general state of public health, as reflected in the statistics on mortality, was not very great until well into the nineteenth century. The drop in mortality (and increase in life expectancy), which started in the previous century in many European countries, is most generally explained in terms of general social and economic conditions, rather than medical innovations.

One of the earliest discoveries of preventive medicine was vaccination. This is generally credited to Edward Jenner, with the date 1796, when he first inoculated an eight-year-old boy with matter from the cowpox vesicles on the hands of a milkmaid. The boy was inoculated for smallpox the following July, and thus shown to be immune to the disease. As with most discoveries, all sorts of anticipations of Jenner's work can be found; but general knowledge of the efficacy of vaccination certainly dates from Jenner, and it was not until after the publication of his account of his experiments in 1798 that large-scale attempts at vaccination were made.

The practice of "variolation," or deliberate inoculation from a mild case of smallpox, had become fashionable in the eighteenth century in many parts of Europe, but this was a very doubtful public health measure. Individuals were perhaps often saved by this deliberate infection, since the death rate after inoculation was said to be, at most, one in 96, as compared with one death for every five or six cases of naturally acquired infection. But a high fee was charged for variolation, which limited it largely to the wealthy; and since the inoculation was with human smallpox, the individuals thus treated may often have been inadvertently responsible for spreading virulent infections.

There is clear evidence of a decline in smallpox mortality, however, following the spread of vaccination with cowpox, after 1800. During the eighteenth century, smallpox had been one of the most important causes of death in all European countries, perhaps responsible for a tenth of all deaths. By 1850 the death rate from smallpox was down to 22 per 1,000 deaths in England, and by the twentieth century it had become a rare cause of death in the Western world, though it remains a serious disease in the Orient and parts of Africa.

The history of the opposition to smallpox vaccination would make an interesting study in resistance to innovation. It started soon after 1800 with violent pamphlets, which were apparently instigated by the doctors who were in danger of losing their large fees for "variolation." "Would not the human character undergo strange mutations if the body were polluted with fluid taken from a cow?" asked the pamphleteers. "What security was there against the growth of horns from the human head?" The questions were made the more worrying by the "authenticated examples" of the pamphleteers. There was "the child at Peckham [who] had its former natural disposition absolutely changed to the brutal, so that it ran upon all fours like a beast, bellowing like a cow, and butted with its head like a bull." There were faces distorted until they resembled those of oxen; there was the lady's daughter who coughed like a cow and the boy who grew patches of cow's hair. These arguments, as K. H. Connell, from whom I have been quoting, points out, "were attractive to a people with so firm a belief in the power of magic in medicine as the Irish" and their effectiveness was probably not limited to Ireland.

The clear statistical evidence of the value of vaccination

gradually won over the medical profession, and then the opposition was taken up "by many patent medicine manufacturers, osteopaths, chiropractors, hydropaths, Christian Scientists, naturopaths and other medical sects," in the words of one medical historian. The loudest recent blasts were from George Bernard Shaw, who seems to have attacked vaccination as one phase in his general war on the silly doctors.

The early methods of vaccination were of course crude, and there must have been many serious mistakes. The theory behind the practice could not be understood until Pasteur and Koch had carried out their studies of immunity seventy-five years later, and until scientific knowledge of viruses started accumulating a hundred years later. The virus of the vaccine still has unexpected and dismaying effects in one out of many thousands of cases, but these rare accidents lose significance in comparison with the removal of smallpox as an ever possible cause of premature death.

Compulsory vaccination, compulsory quarantine, summary dealing with the individual for the protection of the community, still pose nice questions as limitations on our general concept of the freedom of the individual. Though, paradoxically, the individual has surely gained freedom as society has imposed restrictions. He has gained freedom from disease, freedom from many fears, opportunity to lead a fuller life—as he has lost freedom to dispose of waste according to individual idiosyncrasy, lost freedom to roam as a possible source of infection to others.

There is probably some nice balance of freedom here that we need to keep in mind, because the imposition of restrictions for the good of society leads easily to an extreme. As Furnivall has pointed out in his penetrating analysis of British and Dutch colonial policies, public health zeal can reach the extreme where it looks as though the ideal of the public health official would be to have the whole population in jail, so that proper vaccinations, proper diets, proper quarantines, and proper sanitation could be enforced—all, of course, for the good of the population.

The need for laws and for law enforcement is perhaps nowhere clearer than in matters of sanitation. Yet it is surprising to find how recent most of our sanitary measures are. The water systems and drain systems of the Roman cities broke down with the collapse of the Roman political system and remained in disuse through most of the medieval period. The cities were small, hardly more than towns, and the people made shift as they could for water. With the industrial revolution and the beginning of city growth, the supplying of water and the disposal of sewage became imperative needs.

Bernhard Stern has pointed out that "the possibilities of a large water supply in flat countries waited upon the development of pumps, the first of which was installed in Hanover in 1527. A water-power pump was set up in London in 1582 to supply water through lead pipes, and in Paris in 1608. Dutch cities had plentiful water in the seventeenth century. Water supplies were increased by the invention of the steam pump, first installed in London in 1761 and in Paris in 1781." In the United States, there were only 17 waterworks in 1800, all but one privately owned; at the outbreak of the Civil War there were 80 private and 68 publicly owned systems, and the trend toward public ownership has continued with the increasing recognition that the provision of a plentiful and pure water supply is almost necessarily a matter of public concern.

The provision of pure drinking water and the disposal of human wastes, of sewage, are two closely related and equally important aspects of sanitation. Their importance, of course, depends on the whole long catalogue of diseases caused by organisms that get into the body of a new host through the mouth, and out of the body of an old host along with the feces. We made little progress in understanding the precise mechanisms of transmission of diseases, like the dysenteries, typhoid and cholera, until after the development of the germ theory of disease; but the realization of the danger of fecal contamination of water and foods goes way back in the history of mankind.

Many cultures have developed taboos, rituals or customs that were clearly sanitary in effect. Deuteronomy (23:12-13) includes instructions for the burying of feces. The Polynesians and Micronesians had the custom of always defecating over the sea or on the reef. But the aggregation of people into towns and cities created situations in which safe disposal of feces was not easy; and the discovery of the fertilizing value of feces perhaps overrode the ancient taboos. Indeed, it has been pointed out that overcrowded agricultural populations like those of the Orient simply cannot afford to throw away their human wastes—proper sewage disposal is a luxury of an economy of abundance.

Certainly sanitary methods of sewage disposal were slow in developing in modern Europe and America. Down to the middle of the last century, cesspools were the principal means of disposing of human waste; sanitary sewers existed in only a few of the largest cities such as London and Paris, and there only to a limited extent. The cesspools were cleaned privately, when the need was sufficiently urgent.

We have got a sort of stereotype picture of the filth and smells of the Middle Ages, out of which our present cleanliness and sanitation has only gradually emerged. Students of the medieval period, however, have been trying hard to rehabilitate the times that they find so fascinating, and with considerable success. They point out that the towns were mostly small and open, probably much cleaner and more healthful places than we had imagined, and that filth and stench and overcrowding were probably the exception rather than the rule.

The real filth and stench started with the post-medieval growth of the European cities, getting continually worse through the sixteenth, seventeenth and eighteenth centuries, according to this theory. The historians will still allow us to hold our noses at the thought of the gaudy and brilliant courts of that period. And indeed, there is plenty of evidence for the deteriorating sanitation of the growing cities. We owe that very useful contrivance, the water-closet, to one of Queen Elizabeth's courtiers, John Harington, who, fresh from the country, thought something ought to be done about the smells inside the town houses.

Lytton Strachey, in his biographical essay on Harington, describes the event thus:

His nose was sensitive as well as impudent, and he had been made to suffer agonies by the sanitary arrangements in the houses of the great. Suddenly inspired, he invented the water-closet. Then, seizing his pen, he concocted a pamphlet after the manner of Rabelais—or, as he preferred to call him, "the reverent Rabbles"—in which extravagant spirits, intolerable puns, improper stories, and sly satirical digs at eminent personages were blended together into a preposterous rhapsody, followed by an appendix—written, of course, by his servant—could a gentleman be expected to discuss such details?—containing a minute account, with measurements, diagrams and prices, of the new invention. *The Metamorphosis of Ajax*—for so the book, with a crowningly deplorable pun, was entitled—created some sensation. Queen Elizabeth was amused . . . and eventually she set the fashion for the new contrivances by installing one of them in Richmond Palace, with a copy of the *Ajax* hanging from the wall.

(The deplorable pun of Ajax turns on the common Elizabethan word for privy—jakes.)

The water-closet got the stuff out of the house and into the cesspool, but that was a long way from solving the problem of contamination. General sewage systems, even for large cities, are surprisingly recent. As C. E. A. Winslow has pointed out, in his book on *Man and Epidemics:*

Until 1815, the discharge of any waste except kitchen wastes into the drains of London was prohibited by law and the same regulation persisted in Paris up to 1880. Sewerage and sewage disposal date from the epoch-making report of the Health of Town Commission of Great Britain in 1844. This report revealed the accumulation of such an appalling menace of decomposing organic filth that it roused British sanitarians to prompt action. Whereas in 1815 the sewers of London were simply drains to carry off storm water, in 1847 it was made obligatory to discharge all household sewage into them.

In the United States some of the city drainage systems are quite old, but the first comprehensive sewerage project was that designed for Chicago in 1855. For that matter, the whole idea of public health is relatively new, a growth of the last hundred years. One of the pioneers was the German pathologist, Rudolf Virchow, who wrote that "medicine is a social science and politics is nothing else but medicine on a large scale."

In England a prime mover in public health was Edwin Chadwick. His *Report on the Sanitary Condition of the Labouring Population of Great Britain,* published by the Poor Law Commissioners in 1842, led directly to the establishment of official public health agencies in that country. Chadwick was one of the pioneers in the use of statistics as a tool of investigation and persuasion. He found that the average age at death, in Manchester, of members of working-class families was 17 years; of families in trades, 20 years; and of the gentry, 38 years. In Liverpool, the average age at death for the same three classes was 15, 22 and 35. He reported that "More than half of the children of the working classes die, and only one-fifth of the children of the gentry die, before the fifth year of age."

Chadwick was educated for the bar, not for medicine; and the first National Health Board, set up as a consequence of his report, included no physicians, and was far from having the general support of the medical profession. This first board was dissolved after ten years, and not re-created as a centralized health agency until 1871, when it was called the Local Government Board. It finally became the Ministry of Health in 1919.

In the United States, the development of public health is generally considered to have started with a report by Lemuel Shattuck to the Massachusetts Legislature, entitled "A General Plan for the Promotion of Public and Personal Health." As a consequence of the federal form of government, initiative was largely in the hands of states and cities, and developments varied greatly from place to place. Unofficial health agencies, starting with the National Tuberculosis Association in 1900, have been of great importance, particularly through educational campaigns which have built up the "health consciousness" of the people and thus directly or indirectly led to governmental action at different levels. The formation of such associations for a whole array of different diseases has proven an effective way of raising funds for research and treatment— though there surely is a saturation point for drives, however worthy each may be.

The United States Government finally established a Department of Health, Education and Welfare in 1953—the last of the major national governments to form such a ministry.

It is difficult to assess the role of public health in the changing mortality picture of the Western world. Certainly for the past hundred years increasing health services have paralleled an increase in the average length of life. But the increase in longevity seems to have started before health measures were organized or much thought of. That two things occur together is no proof of cause and effect; and many students feel that the beginning, at least, of the change in mortality is most easily explained in terms of general economic and social conditions. In truth, probably a whole series of related but distinguishable trends have tended to reinforce one another to produce the contemporary mortality pattern.

The question of cause and effect here is not entirely a matter of academic interest. It becomes a very practical concern when we set about the problem of helping to "improve" the non-Western world, where the mortality picture today is similar to that of the West a hundred or more years ago. Which of the technologies do we use to bring about the desired change? Is it most important to give agricultural, economic, political, sanitary, medical, industrial, or what kind of aid? These things, of course, are all interrelated; but how could we make a package of them, for export?

Agencies like the Rockefeller Foundation have been attempting to introduce health measures in non-Western areas for something over thirty years now. For the most part, it seems to me that these attempts have not been highly successful in directly measurable terms. The directed campaigns against hookworm or malaria seem rarely to have caught on, and the organizations often collapsed after the withdrawal of foreign personnel and money. The efforts, I think, have been highly "successful" in other, more indirect ways, in providing for culture contact, for experience in study and training programs, in increasing understanding on both sides of the cultural fences. But these, often, have not been the planned objectives.

The failure of such efforts to achieve immediate and dramatic results might be taken as an argument against the single cause theory of health measures and mortality. Recently, however, public health has gained very powerful new tools; and with these, immediate and dramatic results can be obtained.

The insecticide DDT is one such tool, and Ceylon is an example of its effect. An extensive DDT program was started there in 1946 as a malaria control measure. There, as in other similar places, the DDT turned out to affect not only the malaria, but even more dramatically the infant diarrheas, which were apparently in large part fly-carried. At any rate, in the first two years after the beginning of the DDT campaign in Ceylon, the general death rates dropped from 20-22 per 1,000 population to 13-14 per 1,000, and the infant mortality dropped from 135-140 per 1,000 births to 101 in 1947 and 93 in 1948.

Other things besides DDT were happening in Ceylon, but it seems reasonable to regard DDT as the prime agency in this abrupt shift in the mortality trend, particularly since the experience has been paralleled in other places. A single public health measure *can* have a dramatic impact, then, whatever may have been the actual history of developments within the Western countries.

The question of the interrelatedness of things still remains, in another sense. This single technological change has had an abrupt impact on the death rate in Ceylon. And at the same time, the birth rate, already high, has shown slight but regular increase—38.4 births per 1,000 population in 1946, 39.4 in 1947, 40.2 in 1948. This slight increase is possibly also caused by DDT, since the decline in sickness caused by malaria might well be reflected in an increased fertility.

Here, then, we have clear-cut evidence that public health measures can be introduced into a country and can have an immediate and large effect on the rate of population growth in that country. It seems to me out of the question to argue that the public health measures should not be introduced: to argue that is to deny the humanitarian values that are surely man's most precious possession. And anyway, the Western nations cannot directly withhold any public health measure, except perhaps where they govern as colonial powers. The knowledge and the chemicals are public property as open to the use of the Ceylonese as of the Swiss, who made the discovery in the case of DDT.

The public health measures are, however, in large part a product of Western science, and Western technicians can undoubtedly be helpful in aiding their diffusion. About all that we can hope is that both local people and Western technicians will try to keep an awareness of the total situation, and at least think about the fertility problem as they deal with the mortality problem.

I have tried, in this chapter, to support the thesis that there is not a direct cause-and-effect relationship between public health and population growth in the West. I don't know whether any single "cause" for population growth could be isolated— it seems to be a result of complex economic, social, political and geographical factors. Public health, like the population growth itself, can be looked at as one of the products of the general course of Western development.

Within the West, as mortality has declined, as public health has developed, patterns of fertility control have also developed, though with a minimum of overt aid from scientific discovery. If we are going to try to help with the establishment of one part of this pattern in other cultural contexts, shouldn't we try also to help with compensating aspects of the pattern— with, specifically, fertility control, as well as with economic and industrial techniques? Shouldn't contraception be as much a public health concern as vaccination?

I have come to feel that the research aspects of these questions, at least, should be a matter of general and public concern. This is a long way from saying that I think reproduction should be tied up with governmental bureaucracy, so that, say, a license would be required for each addition to the family. Reproduction surely doesn't require rigid control in the sense that smallpox does. But it needs study as much as smallpox.

But that is getting off the track. I have wanted, in this book, to describe what people have done, not what they ought to do. So far we have discussed reproduction and mortality. The population—the number of people—clearly results from the relations between the birth rates and the death rates. The size of the population that any given region can support depends on the economic activities of the population, on the means of subsistence, on the nature of the culture. The happiness or well-being of the population, and of the individuals that compose it, clearly also depends on these economic and cultural factors.

But all of this presupposes a closed system, and the only closed system we have, insofar as human populations are concerned, is the earth itself. If we look at any smaller system, at any nation, continent or region, the population is a result not only of fertility and mortality, but of emigration and immigration, of movement into and out of the region. If we look at economics or culture, at the means of subsistence, we also find that no region is an island unto itself, but that every economy, to be understood, must be related to other economies.

In the last several chapters we have been looking, first at fertility, then at mortality. To complete the picture, then, we should now give some consideration to the geographical movement of population, to migration.

CHAPTER *13* MIGRATION

I once heard the economist Kenneth Boulding say that a population is a collection of similar items enclosed by a picket fence of definition. The items can get inside the fence by being born there; they can escape by death; and they can jump over the fence in either direction by migrating.

The importance of this fence-jumping varies, of course, with the kind of fence, and the kinds of items being fenced in. With human population, the fence-jumping process of migration can rarely be ignored. Occasionally populations are isolated on islands for considerable lengths of time; occasionally governments create powerful barriers, as in Japan during the Shogunate when leaving the country was a crime punishable by death. But generally man has tended to wander, and neither seas nor governments have been effective in stopping him.

The wanderings of men have been of many different sorts. During the historic period there have been several mass move-

190

ments of peoples like those of the Huns and the Turks toward
Europe, and these perhaps come first to mind in association
with the word "migration." In terms of sheer numbers, however, the greatest population movement of all has been that
out of Europe during the nineteenth century when something
like sixty million people left that continent, going chiefly to
the Americas, Australia and South Africa. Yet this could hardly
be called a "mass movement," because it was made up of individuals, families, and small groups from many different places,
moving from many different motives.

The mass movements, like those of the Huns, have caught
our imagination, making us prone to interpret migration in
such terms. But I suspect that, from a geological point of view,
such movements must be relatively new. They are hardly possible except with a considerable and organized population, and
large organized populations are post-Neolithic developments,
arising from the invention of agriculture and husbandry.

Yet man spread almost everywhere over the land surface
of the globe back in the Old Stone Age, in a food-gathering
stage of culture, when, presumably, the largest social unit was
the band or tribe of a few score individuals occupying some
rather small and definite traditional territory. Migration under
those conditions must have been quite different.

The best chance to observe Stone Age conditions on a
continental scale has been in Australia. There the aborigines,
in the words of the Australian anthropologist, Norman Tindale,

were nomadic within a tribal area, and were closely tied to this
territory by the continuous necessity of gathering the day's food
and spending the greater part of each day doing so, leaving little
time for other activities, save at a few especially favorable seasons
of the year. They had limited means of travel and, should they
wish to move from their living area, faced ecological barriers and
physical obstructions as well as hostile opposition from armed
owners of adjoining tribal territories. They suffered also psychologi-

cal fears if they came to trespass on unknown territories, and when confronted with new foods they had not previously encountered. Despite their continual wanderings they were not widely travelled.

But shifts of population do occur under these circumstances. To continue quoting from Dr. Tindale:

The Pintubi tribe, in common with the Pitjandjara and Jumu, have made considerable south-eastward movements, of the order of 50 to 100 miles during the past several generations; their latest shifts were initiated in 1916, after a severe drought forced them to travel away from their usual territory. The Pitjandjara, for example, in usurping the present eastern half of their country, ambushed and killed many Jangkundjara. About one-half of the surviving Jangkundjara shifted their living area to the vicinity of Ooldea to escape the Pitjandjara. . . .

A movement of a hundred miles in three generations seems to us no movement at all; but with food-gathering man, we can deal with time on the geological scale. Shifts of a hundred miles in a hundred years could add up to very great changes indeed over ten thousand years, and we have many tens of thousands of years in which to get man distributed over the globe.

One anthropologist, Sir Arthur Keith, has been so impressed by the immobility of food-gathering man that he concludes that the various human "races" must have evolved pretty much in their present areas of distribution, with the Chinese descending from Peking man, the Javanese from Java man, the modern Africans from various Africa fossil types, the Europeans from Neanderthal man, and so forth. The fact that the modern races resemble each other more than these presumed ancestors he would explain as "convergence" or as the result of blending and blurring of racial boundaries in comparatively recent times.

This is an extreme position, which seems to me not at all justified by what we know about population movements and territoriality in mammals in general or man in particular. The movements of man in the Pleistocene surely were very slow so that it is misleading to think of "invasions" from Asia or Africa into Europe or vice versa. Some word like "infiltration" would probably describe the process more accurately. If such shifts averaged out at a rate of fifty or a hundred miles every three or four generations, there would be plenty of time for great spread and considerable mixing all over the land mass of the Old World in the latter part of the Pleistocene. The present pattern of deserts, a considerable barrier to human movement, is surely a product of the last glacial retreat, and hence not important over the time span here considered.

The movement was slow, most breeding surely was within limited and small populations, hence there was ample opportunity for the development and maintenance of human diversity. But no people—at least no surviving people—lived long enough in complete isolation from other men to become a different species, something physiologically and genetically separated from the general pool of human heredity.

Our *sapiens* ancestors were probably the most capable and the most mobile of the manlike primates, and as they filtered out over the Afro-Eurasian land mass, they probably exterminated all of the other manlike animals that they couldn't breed with. There was likely considerable of both—of killing and of breeding—with these slow shifts of population. And the result is a pattern of physical diversity; but to me, at least, this diversity of men is less striking than the underlying uniformity. We can thus see how an adaptable animal like man could come to occupy a good part of the continental land masses of the Old World long before he had developed any very complex cultural equipment. The leopard achieved about the same distribution without any help from culture.

But what about Australia, America and the islands of the Pacific?

There is an immense amount of speculation about the antiquity of man in America, and about how he got there. There are also a few facts, but not enough for a clear reconstruction of the past.

Man must have been in America for a very long time. At the time the continents were "discovered" by the Europeans, they were inhabited from Tierra del Fuego to Alaska by peoples showing considerable physical diversity from region to region, showing very great diversity in languages and culture— the sort of diversity that takes many thousands of years to develop. The time scale, however, would be in tens of thousands rather than hundreds of thousands of years, because the Americans were all of the same general physical type as the peoples of eastern Asia—"Mongoloid." The Americans were modern men, not descendants of some separate, ancient manlike stock, and not isolated from the men of Asia long enough to allow evolutionary divergence.

North America has been almost as thoroughly ransacked by paleontologists, archeologists, and amateur naturalists as Europe, yet no fossils of men or apes have ever been found. This negative evidence led many anthropologists to insist that man must be a "recent" arrival in America. There is still no evidence for anything except modern man in America, but increasingly students are coming to think that this modern man must have first arrived back in Pleistocene time.

There is a general agreement that man got to America by way of Siberia and Alaska—a bleak enough route now, but the country was probably quite different at the time of man's first crossing. On a clear day, Asia and America are within sight of one another at the Bering Strait, and two islands in the middle of the strait (Big and Little Diomede) cut the crossing down to two easy 25-mile stretches. The greatest

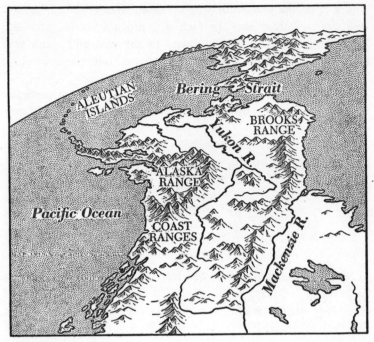

PROBABLE ROUTE FROM ASIA OF THE FIRST AMERICANS

depth of water in the strait now is 120 feet, and it is likely that during parts of the Pleistocene this was dry land, so that man and animals could cross without resorting to boats. The first crossing of man to America over this route may have taken place something like 25,000 years ago, when much of North America was covered by thick glaciers, which held enough of the earth's water frozen to lower the seas to the point of transforming the Bering Strait into an isthmus.

It seems absurd at first sight to think that man could have been crossing this Bering Isthmus when so much of North America even down to Wisconsin and Michigan was covered with ice; but studies over the last few years in Alaska have shown that this glaciation was far from a uniform affair, and that this particular area, in fact, was probably open grassland abounding in game, while country to the east and south was covered with ice. As Ralph Solecki points out:

That the game animals on which [man] depended had preceded him over this route is amply proved by their fossil remains. Paleontologists have found in Alaska fossils of the bison, musk ox, goat, moose, woolly mammoth, mastodon and many other animals that appear to have originated not in America but in Eurasia. Some of these fossils are 25,000 to 30,000 years old, showing that the animals had made the crossing well before man. Alaska must have been a lush animal habitat in those days; all over the territory there are abundant ancient remains of horse, deer, antelope, wolf, bear and beaver, as well as the newcomers from Asia.

Man, then, could easily wander back and forth from Asia to America following game. But how did he get past the great glaciers to reach the southern parts of the continent? To quote Dr. Solecki again:

William A. Johnston of the Canadian Geological Survey believes that the most favorable route was over the low-level northern coast-line of Alaska to the Mackenzie River and then down that valley. . . . The Mackenzie valley and a broad belt down through the continent east of the Rockies are believed to have been free of ice at an early stage, probably about 25,000 to 30,000 years ago.

It is some 11,000 miles from the Bering Strait to Tierra del Fuego—and it seems to me quite possible that it took man 11,000 years to filter down the length of these two continents. The climates of particular regions, especially in the north and the south, may have been different when man first came in; but they would always have been varied, so that man, in the process of infiltration, would have had to learn to adapt to grasslands and mountains and deserts and rain forests, learn to use new foods and to avoid new enemies. He couldn't just walk from Alaska to Chile: he would have to develop new cultural adaptations with each new environment, and push on into strange environments as population pressures built up, or new food possibilities pulled.

In the first wave, at least, the governing factors would be man and nature; but soon relations between man and man would come to operate, with less aggressive, less efficient cultures pushed into marginal areas and movement everywhere restricted by the patterns of territorial and cultural adjustments. The interchange would be so little that the great civilizations of Central America and the Andes could be built up with no knowledge of each other, and with almost a minimum of indirect exchange of cultural traits, so that they seem almost as separate from one another as they are from the contemporary civilizations of the Old World.

As for Australia, there is no question about land bridges: man must have got there over water. He and the dog were the only mammals that managed this since the days when marsupials were the latest thing in mammalian design. The Australians, unlike the Americans, represent a racial stock quite distinct from any now living elsewhere, though Australian-like features can be found in a few Asiatic peoples, such as the Veddas of Ceylon.

The Australians surely got there by way of the East Indies, but they were either exterminated or pushed out of these islands by later invasions of Melanesian and Indonesian peoples. There may have been several "invasions" of Australia, since there is some physical diversity within the "race." The firstcomers may have been the ancestors of the Tasmanians, who got pushed to the habitable extremity of land some time ago, and who finally became extinct in 1879 when the last survivor died in the face of the latest Caucasian invasion.

The East Indies and tropical Asia have been the scene of many invasions, migrations and infiltrations of people, judging by the diversity of the present inhabitants, who show in varying proportions the characteristics of all of the major racial stocks. It is an interesting problem in deduction to try to figure out what might have happened by examining the present distribution and characteristics of peoples like the Negritos, Melanesians and Indonesians; but about the only firm conclusion is that this has been a mixing pot, if not a melting pot, of mankind for a very long time.

The last of the major migratory movements here was that of the Polynesians out into the Pacific. The anthropological evidence is overwhelmingly in favor of an Asiatic origin for these people—the thrilling exploit of the Kon-Tiki expedition notwithstanding—but precisely where they came from remains a mystery, as does why they started moving. The later movements, to Hawaii and to New Zealand, can be reconstructed with some probability of accuracy from legends.

The Polynesians, during the period of their Pacific migrations, had a relatively advanced culture. If cultural stages were taken literally, they were in a "stone age"; but this clearly was because stone, shell and bones were the only materials available on their islands. Their culture in other ways was complex enough so that, in their dealings with the environment, they were a long way from the food-gathering peoples of the Pleistocene. Their migrations, explorations and conquests, then, probably differ correspondingly from earlier population shifts of the Pleistocene peoples. They seem more like the population movements that have occurred in Europe and the Near East in historic times.

Europe has certainly had an extraordinarily varied population history, depending in part on the advances and retreats of the glaciers, and the consequent shifts in habitability through the Pleistocene, but depending also in part upon events to the south and east which led to outward movements of people to this marginal area. Neanderthal man gave way to Cro-Magnon man, who gave way in turn to successive physical and cultural varieties of modern man. Some of the greatest shifts probably occurred just a little before the opening of history, as the Sahara and regions to the east changed from grassland to desert with the climatic changes of the last glacial retreat. But the population shifts continued right on down to the invasion of the Osmanli Turks in the sixteenth century.

The character of the movements may have changed gradually, from the jostling, infiltering bands of food-gatherers to the organized mass invasions of armies and peoples that we read about in history.

Then, after the sixteenth century, the tables were turned, and the European peoples started conquering and invading the rest of the world, setting off population movements on scales of distance, numbers and time, quite different from anything that had gone on before. It is this new kind of movement that demographers mean when they write about migration.

The largest movement has been from Europe to North America, involving a total of perhaps 45 million persons. Many of these returned to Europe, but the majority settled permanently in the new country. Some 20 million Europeans, mostly from Spain, Portugal and Italy, have migrated to South and Central America, again with the overwhelming majority staying. Something over 4 million, mostly from the British Isles, have migrated to Australia. Migrations to South Africa, the East Indies and other parts of the world have been considerably smaller, especially in terms of permanent settlement. The South African population of European origin, in 1951, was somewhat over 2.5 million.

The movement out from Europe has been the largest of the modern migrations, but far from the only one. The next in size has been the involuntary movement out of Africa. Statistics on the slave trade are far from precise, but clearly many millions of persons were involved: Carr-Saunders puts the figure at 20 millions. Some of these died in the course of shipment, some were sold in Europe and Asia, but something like 15 million were imported into the Americas—less than a million in the sixteenth century, 3 million in the seventeenth, 7 million in the eighteenth and 4 million in the nineteenth. Most of these went to the Caribbean or South America, and it seems probable that only about a million Negro slaves were ever imported into the United States or regions that later became part of the United States.

Migration from China has been mostly to neighboring parts of Asia—to Formosa, Java, Thailand, Malaya and the like. Something like 200,000 have emigrated to America (as compared with several million to neighboring Asiatic areas), and some 54,000 have settled in Europe.

Migration from India has also been largely to other Asiatic countries. In 1945 it was estimated that there were about a million Indians in Burma, 750,000 in Ceylon, about the same number in Malaya, 300,000 in Mauritius, 100,000 in Fiji, 300,000 in Trinidad and British Guiana, and 100,000 in British colonies in Africa.

In addition to these long-distance movements, there have been many population shifts within continents, within nations and between neighboring nations in modern times. The westward movement of population within the United States is one example, and the movement from country to city in the United States and in other countries is another example. There have been similar shifts in Russia.

A new kind of migration has appeared in Europe as a consequence of the two world wars—the forced shifting of people in accordance to political boundary changes, or in accordance with dictates of governmental policy. The population exchange between Greece and Turkey after World War I is an example.

About 1,200,000 Greeks were moved from Turkish territory as a result of the arrangements of the Convention of Lausanne of 1923, and some 600,000 Turks were moved from various Balkan countries, mostly from Greece. There was a smaller exchange between Greece and Bulgaria.

These attempts to solve the "Balkan problem" by forced transference of peoples to make nationalities and languages correspond to political boundaries did not seem very successful at the time I lived in the Balkans in the nineteen-thirties. The situation was typified for me by the region around Lake Presba, a beautiful highland lake where I often went to collect mosquitoes. The boundaries of Greece, Yugoslavia and Albania met in the middle of the lake; but the villages on the lake shore were composed of people who spoke Bulgarian and thought of themselves as Bulgarians. There were, similarly, Greek-speaking villages in Albania, and Albanian-speaking villages in many parts of Greece. In the face of this mixture of languages and cultural traditions, the attempt to form a neat pattern of national states seemed hopeless.

Yet the idea of moving populations to conform to political boundaries is a continuing fashion. Germany managed some major population shifts just before and during the period of World War II—including some five million Jews shifted to extermination camps. After the war, the Allies continued the shifting by shipping Germans from many areas back to Germany, and in the Far East by returning Japanese settlers to their country of origin. The formation of the nation of Israel has involved considerable shifts of both Arabs and Jews. The catalogue of these forced population movements in recent years is long, and involves staggering numbers of people as well as a staggering sum of human misery.

Probably the general label of migration should cover temporary population shifts as well as these more permanent changes and transplantations. There are a variety of such temporary movements: the shifts of pastoral tribes between summer and winter pastures; the seasonal migration of labor in many parts of the world; the foreign residence of colonial administrators and other officers of business and government; the distant movements of expeditionary armies. These migrations, even though temporary, may have many effects on the prevalence of different sorts of people through culture contacts and changes, and through the biological mixture of genes.

If we exclude these recurrent or temporary sorts of migrations, we still have, as we have seen, a considerable variety of quite different population movements. These might be grouped under six headings: 1, the dispersal of food-gathering man; 2, the more or less organized movements of hordes or tribes; 3, slave-trading; 4, modern intercontinental migration; 5, drifts within major population areas; and 6, forced transplantations.

It seems to me that the dispersal of food-gathering man (discussed first in this chapter) can be studied in much the same way as the dispersal of other mammals. Cultural factors probably became increasingly important in enabling one group of men to displace another, but the whole process may not have been greatly unlike, say, the dispersal of squirrels, where we can see major population shifts occurring in the United States at the present time. Biological factors like territoriality, population pressures, climatic and food adaptations were probably of great importance.

The large tribal movements that we see at the dawn of history and that have continued over so much of the historic period, seem different from this in that they involve fairly large and organized populations, the sort of populations that could not be formed until after the Neolithic development of agriculture and animal husbandry. The "barbarians" that so pestered the Mediterranean world were not simple, food-gathering "savages"; they were people who had long since passed into a

Neolithic stage of economy. Their movements may still have
been influenced by factors that could be classed as "biological,"
like population pressures, but the general pattern of barbarian
invasion of the Graeco-Roman world, and the similar disturbances in the eastern empire, can most profitably be studied
in terms of cultural and historical forces.

I think slave-trading should be looked at as a special variety
of population movement. Here, certainly, we have parted company with biological factors and entered a purely cultural
sphere. The effects of the African slave trade on American
population are obvious enough, but this is only the most spectacular case of a rather widespread phenomenon. The Old World
civilizations all involved a considerable transference of peoples
under slave terms, and alien slave elements probably generally became absorbed into the master populations. The slave
labor of contemporary totalitarian governments also involves
population movement, but this is probably best treated as something quite distinct from the old-fashioned, individual kind of
slavery.

The intercontinental migrations of the past few centuries are
yet another kind of population movement, and this is the
kind on which demographers have focused most attention. It
has been a movement of individuals and families and sometimes small religious or economic groups from scattered parts
of their home country to remote parts of the world. The
cumulative effect, both on population patterns and cultural
patterns, has been tremendous, but the forces governing the
movement—economic, religious, political—have been so diverse
that generalization is difficult.

In general the movement has been from areas of dense
population to areas of low population. But any such statement
has to be hedged with all sorts of qualifications. The Egyptians,
who for many centuries have been densely crowded in their
delta and narrow valley, have never attempted to escape the

poverty and misery of their homeland by emigration. Instead, peoples from less crowded lands have moved in on them— Greeks, Italians, Arabs, Sudanese, Jews. Mexico and Peru were probably as densely populated as Spain when the Spaniards started moving in. This would be different from Greeks and Italians going to Egypt, since the Spaniards came in as conquerors, though Egypt too has had much experience with conquerors who have come and stayed.

It would probably be safer to say that, in general, emigration has been from areas where the possibilities for individual economic advancement seemed hopeless to areas where they seemed bright, the hopelessness or brightness being seen through various sorts of cultural spectacles. This overlooks things like the religious motivations of the Puritans and the political motivations of the people who left Germany in the eighteen-forties. But these were moving from areas where the religious or political outlook seemed dim to areas where it seemed bright —which is similar to the economic statement.

The newest variety of migration is the forced transplantation of peoples so arrogantly practiced by Nazi Germany. This included the transplantation of population elements listed as "undesirable" to extermination camps, where human population could be converted into plant fertilizer, so that the breed of men could be purified and improved. Nazi Germany is an extreme case, and perhaps no extreme should be used in judging an idea, since almost anything can be reduced to an absurdity, or extended to a tragedy. The Nazi experiment, nevertheless, may serve us here as a convenient transition from our look at migration to our look at eugenics, at the general idea of trying to improve the breed of men, the quality of the human population.

CHAPTER *14* THE IDEA OF EUGENICS

So far in this book, we have been dealing with problems of the quantity of people. What about the quality? Man has been extraordinarily successful in breeding bigger raspberries and cows that produce large quantities of milk; why not breed men of superlative intelligence? We lavish a great deal of attention on the improvement of our chickens, pigs and wheat, and leave our own fate to the whims of romantic love, or the strategy of dowry, or the satisfaction of the moment's concupiscence.

Not only are we doing nothing to improve ourselves; maybe we are actually promoting our deterioration by coddling the weak, repairing the malformed, allowing the feeble-minded to implant their semen in any womb that will receive it. Meanwhile, the bright people, the members of the best families with their fine biological inheritance, are failing to reproduce themselves because of the oconomic burden of raising and educating many children. "Natural laws" which would prune the weak, stupid and undesirable, and promote the survival of the fittest, are thus violated, and mankind is going to the dogs.

It is easy to poke fun at the eugenicists, partly because they are such earnest and serious people and partly because a few of them have gone to absurd lengths in attributing human behavior to genetic inheritance and in classifying "desirable" and "undesirable" kinds of people. The whole question is overlaid with emotional and propaganda accretions about differences in races, differences in classes, differences in families. But there is a very real question under all of this: are we deteriorating genetically because of the nature of our civilization and is there anything we can or should do about it?

I don't know of any clear evidence of genetic deterioration in contemporary populations. As far as physique is concerned, people in the Western world are improving. The size of medieval armor is often mentioned to show what runts our ancestors were, even those of the best families; and there are measurements over the years on incoming freshmen at Yale to show that we are growing taller and perhaps more powerful. No one, of course, attributes this to any improvement in biological inheritance: the potentialities have always been there, and they are being realized now because of better nutrition, more healthful living conditions, and the like.

When we move from physical condition to mental condition, the evidence is much less clear, much more difficult to evaluate. The British, in 1944, set up a Royal Commission on Population to take a thorough look at the present population situation in Great Britain and at its future prospects. The Report of this Commission, published in 1949, covered not only questions of numbers of people, but also the question of the quality of the people.

The Commission consulted a number of experts and reviewed many studies and found "a remarkable approach to agreement among them on the two essential points, (1) that a considerable element in intelligence is inherited, and (2) that the more intelligent have smaller families on the average than others." The deduction from these two propositions would be that there has been a continuing loss of intelligence from Western populations during the last century or so of widespread family limitation. The various attempts to measure this loss "all point to a rather serious drop in average intelligence with a more than corresponding increase in mental deficiency and decrease of high intelligence."

The largest and most thorough attempt at measurement, however, turned up with the opposite result. Intelligence tests were given to 87,498 eleven-year-old children in Scotland in 1932; and similar tests to 70,805 children of corresponding age in 1947. The mean score in 1947 was higher than in 1932, "boys having increased 1.3 points and girls no less than 3.2 points of score."

With these Scottish tests, as with all of the others, there was a correlation between family size and intelligence: children from smaller families showing, on the average, significantly higher scores than children from larger families. The trouble is, of course, that we don't know the meaning of this intelligence difference between children from small and large families. It may be again that better nutrition, better living conditions, better educational opportunities for children in small families are reflected in the test performance; and improvements in these same sorts of things over fifteen years may be the explanation of the Scottish figures.

The Royal Commission drew about the only conclusion possible from the present evidence: "There is an immediate need for further research into the effect of the differential birth rate on the average level of intelligence of the nation, and we consider that direct investigation in other parts of the country on the lines of the Scottish inquiry . . . together with research into the respective influences of environment and heredity in intelligence and the effectiveness of the tests by which these factors are assessed should be generously encouraged by the Government."

Intelligence tests have become very widely used in recent years, and they have proved their usefulness and reliability in many sorts of situations. With children from closely comparable environments—similar income group, similar educational opportunity, similar parental attitudes and so forth— differences in the tests probably reflect to a considerable degree innate differences among the children, inherited differences in some sort of mental aptitude. But I doubt whether anyone believes that we have any test that will reveal absolute differences—that will measure, say, the difference between a ten-year-old child from the family of a physician living in an American suburb and a ten-year-old child from one of the households on an atoll in Micronesia.

This brings us to the old problem of the relative roles of "nature versus nurture" in the explanation of differences in human intelligence, aptitudes and accomplishment. The pairing of "nature" and "nurture," of heredity and environment, is in some ways meaningless, since each individual is the result of a set of genetic potentialities developing in some environment. We can't sort out one batch of traits and call them genetic, and another batch of traits and call them environmental; we can only, in the case of any trait, try to assess its environmental and genetic components. Some traits, like eye color, seem to be entirely genetic, with environment having no appreciable influence on the expression of the genetic potentiality; while other traits, like a taste for ripe olives, seem to be entirely environmental. But most traits of physique, or behavior, in which men differ, seem to be a blend of both kinds of influences.

With intelligence we get all sorts of added complications

because of the nature of the concept. It certainly is not a single trait that can be studied as a unit, and it is also not clear that we have succeeded in breaking it down into meaningful unit traits, despite all of the work that has been done on this problem. Aspects like verbal ability, abstracting ability, manipulative ability, visualizing ability, and memory appear to be rather different sorts of things and may be the results of rather different sorts of genetic potentials and environmental influences; but these things are still too intangible for any clear genetic analysis.

Breeding experiments under controlled environmental conditions—the sort of study that would be used with other animals to isolate genetic factors—are out of the question with man. But human society presents us with various sorts of unplanned experiments, and a great deal can be learned by the judicious study of these situations. One of the most valuable of these situations is provided by twins. We have identical (one egg) and fraternal (two-egg) twins. The identical twins, derived from the union of a single egg and sperm, have identical genetic potentialities, whereas the two-egg twins have the same sort of differences in heredity as any other pair of brothers and sisters.

Identical twins are occasionally adopted separately into foster homes, and in such cases we have a chance to study the effect of different environments on the same genetic potentiality. Identical twins reared together form a convenient comparison, or "control" for such study, and further comparisons can be made with fraternal twins reared together and separately.

In the most extensive twin study so far made, twenty pairs of one-egg twins who had been raised separately were studied, and comparisons were made with fifty pairs of one-egg twins who had been reared together and with fifty pairs of two-egg twins (but of the same sex) who had been reared together. With the Binet I.Q. test the average difference between one-egg twins reared together was 5.3 points, while the average difference between such twins when reared apart was 8.2 points. Two-egg twins reared together showed an average difference of 9.9 points. In another sort of test, the Stanford achievement test, the one-egg twins reared apart showed a greater difference than the two-egg twins reared together. These, and many other similar observations, tend to show that "mental ability, though undoubtedly influenced by heredity, is less fixed and more liable to modification by environment than most physical traits," to quote the conclusions of Dunn and Dobzhansky in their book on *Heredity, Race and Society*.

Thus, while there is no question but what intelligence, as we measure it, tends to be lower among members of large families than among members of small families in our culture, this is just as likely (or perhaps more likely) due to the unfavorable environment, in the sense of lessened educational opportunity, lessened parental care and the like, as to unfavorable genetic potentialities.

There are also many studies which show that "intelligence," as measured by various sorts of tests, varies with social class or with income group—children from families of higher income or social status tending to be, on the average, more "intelligent." This, of course, is closely related to family size, since the higher economic or social groups also, in our culture, tend to have smaller families. It thus seems that the "unintelligent" are breeding much faster than the "intelligent."

Here again we face the problem of disentangling cause and effect. Do people achieve higher income status because they are more intelligent, or is the better performance on intelligence tests a result of the better opportunities for training and education? The leaders of the eugenics movement, from Francis Galton on, have tended to assume that "of course" intelligence was the cause. In Galton's words: "It follows that the men who achieve eminence, and those who are naturally capable, are, to a large extent, identical. I have shown that social hindrances cannot impede men of high ability from becoming eminent. I shall now maintain that social advantages are incompetent to give that status to a man of moderate ability."

But one of our leading geneticists, H. J. Muller, who won the Nobel prize for his discovery of the influence of X-rays on mutation rates, can take quite a different point of view. "It could at least as well be maintained," Muller has written, "that the dominant classes tend to have the genetic equipment which would be least desirable in a well-ordered social system, since they have been selected chiefly on the basis of predatory, rather than truly constructive behavior. The 'respectable' captain of industry, military leader or politician, and the successful gangster are psychologically not so far apart. The high-minded, the scrupulous, the idealistic, the generous and those who are too intelligent to wish to confine their interests to their personal monetary success, these are apt to be left behind in the present-day battle."

All of this concerns the ordinary, or normal range of human intelligence and ability, where the evaluation of desirable and undesirable traits is difficult and subject to large differences of opinion. There are, however, many traits that everyone agrees are undesirable—especially the various kinds of feeble-mindedness and insanity. Are these a result of genetic inheritance, and are they increasing or liable to increase in our population?

A word like "feeble-minded" covers a multitude of sins. As we all know, there is every gradation between the very bright child, the perfectly competent child, the dull and slow child, the definitely "backward" child, the "feeble-minded" child, and the moron, the idiot and the imbecile. All sorts of efforts have been made to give reasonably precise meanings to such words and to find measurements and criteria that would enable us to sort out meaningful categories from this continuum. One textbook definition of feeble-mindedness covers:

Persons in whose cases there exists mental defectiveness which, though not amounting to imbecility, is yet so pronounced that they require care, supervision and control for their own protection or for the protection of others, or, in the case of children, that they appear to be permanently incapable by reason of such defectiveness of receiving proper benefit from the instruction in ordinary schools.

The I.Q. tests have proven to be useful in describing such conditions, which are generally characterized by scores below 70. At the extreme end of the spectrum, with the idiots and the imbeciles, we find a well-defined series of clinical entities like "microcephalic idiots," "Mongolian idiots" and "cretins" which can be diagnosed and studied.

Some kinds of feeble-mindedness and idiocy are clearly due to environmental accidents of one sort or another, like infection or injury; many of them are clearly the result of hereditary defects; and in others the presumptive evidence for a hereditary basis is strong. There is little argument about the undesirability of allowing imbeciles and the feeble-minded to reproduce for social as well as eugenic reasons. Where such individuals are confined in institutions, reproduction is pretty much automatically under control. Where confinement does not seem necessary, and the defect has a hereditary basis, sterilization would certainly seem advisable, and laws to this effect are already in operation in many states and countries. Modern sterilization methods in no way interfere with the emotional or physical life of the individual beyond preventing conception, and surely society has the right to interfere with this.

Much the same line of reasoning applies to the insane. There are, however, many varieties of insanity, and with most of these we are still uncertain about the relative roles of genetics and environmental factors in producing the deranged condition. In the commonest form of mental disease, schizophrenia, there is clearly some sort of an hereditary disposition. Of sixty-two pairs of identical twins in whom schizophrenia was found, both twins were schizophrenic in two-thirds of the cases; whereas with fraternal twins both were schizophrenic in only eleven per cent of the cases. If the disease were entirely hereditary, where one identical twin was schizophrenic, the other would always also show the disease; if it were entirely environmental, one would expect no greater agreement in the case of identical twins than in the case of fraternal twins.

The human genetic make-up is so diverse, and the various desirable and undesirable (by whatever definition) genes are so broadly scattered through the population that the effect of any eugenic program would be very slow—and conversely, the effects of failing to apply any eugenic program would be equally slow. In a world full of immediate threats, the threat of genetic deterioration of man seems remote. This, I think, is one of the basic points that the two eminent geneticists, L. C. Dunn and Th. Dobzhansky, have tried to make in their little book on the subject, *Heredity, Race and Society*.

The people who are alarmed about the present threat of genetic deterioration in man often sound as though this were something new, a side product of our present industrial civilization in which the ordinary force of "natural selection" in keeping the race up to the mark was being nullified. I think this is questionable.

They speak of various "dysgenic" effects, which, on the one hand, tend to promote the survival and even encourage the reproduction of the unfit; and which, on the other hand, tend to impede the reproduction of many desirable groups and individuals. Their picture of present conditions is certainly plausible enough, and I do not want to argue that man tends to act in his best interests, from the biological point of view.

My only argument is that this behavior does not seem to me particularly new—that man has been acting in ways contrary to his best interests for a very long time. This may very well prove disastrous for the species in the near future. The puzzle, really, is how he has been able to get along so well so far.

War is clearly a dysgenic force in that it gathers together the finest physical and mental specimens of a people at the time of the height of their reproductive powers and arbitrarily kills off large numbers of them, and prevents normal family relations among the rest for appreciable periods of time. Meanwhile, those rejected on physical or mental grounds are left at home to perpetuate the race.

These dysgenic influences have been systematized in modern times through the system of conscript armies and through the increasing size of armies in relation to noncombatant populations. This may represent an intensification of the dysgenic force, but still the general principle of war acting as an agent of unnatural selection has been in force for a very long time.

Maybe way back in the Pleistocene, war, or the general homicidal tendency, was a force of "natural" selection. One can visualize the most intelligent and the most agile men succeeding in preserving their own heads while they garnered heads from their tribal enemies; conversely, the dull and stupid would be eliminated in their first adolescent skirmishes. This sort of thing might well favor bloodthirstiness as well as intelligence, and may account for much that is deplorable in human nature.

But these possibly favorable effects of homicide began to disappear way back in the Neolithic when war presumably started to become systematized and when survival value would presumably go to the Spartan tradition. For a very long time now war has not tended to promote the survival of physical or intellectual types that we would regard as highly desirable.

Differential fertility, whereby the better-educated and the more prosperous tend to have fewer children, is, in its contemporary form, a new phenomenon. It may also be a transient phenomenon. The Royal Commission that looked into these matters in England found that the small-family pattern was tending to spread to the lower income groups as knowledge of contraception and awareness of the difficulty of properly raising many children increased. At the same time, the upper income groups were tending to have more children, tending to have as many children as they thought they could afford. This may be a response to a feeling that a family of several children provides a "healthier" living environment than the one-child or two-child family at one time so prevalent. Most of us who were "only" children feel that we missed something important, and we want to give our own children the benefit of fraternal companionship (and rivalry)—if we can afford it.

The alarmists are worried about the dysgenic effect of this new and possibly transient differential family pattern. Relatively little attention, however, has been paid to a similar force of negative selection that has been in operation for a long time— the celibacy of the priesthood. One would think that this, over the last 1,900 years in Europe, would have had an appreciable effect on the genetic constitution of several European populations, if any eugenic program can be effective. For generation after generation the people with inclinations for scholarship, for quiet and peace, for all sorts of pursuits which most of us would take to indicate "favorable" traits, entered monasteries and nunneries and were removed from the reproducing population. The effect of this, particularly during the Middle Ages, must have been enormous—despite the occasional leakage of genes from the monastic population reflected in some of the more scandalous stories of the times.

There may have been a real genetic effect from this ideal of celibacy. I have heard one friend express the opinion that the decline of intellectual leadership in Italy after the Renaissance may have been a result of this long-term negative selection, though probably few people would agree with such an explanation.

The Christian ideal of celibacy is not unique as a dysgenic force, and one could probably collect many examples of man behaving in a manner that, biologically, would seem irrational. Infanticide is sometimes quoted as an example of ancient eugenics, and certainly the congenitally deformed were destroyed at birth in many cultures. But it would be very difficult to assess the potentialities of a newborn infant except for obvious deformities that would probably, in any case, prevent the individual from growing up to form part of the reproductive population, so that I would doubt whether infanticide has ever really been effective as a eugenic force. It may more frequently have been dysgenic when human sacrifice was involved, because the gods would hardly be appeased by an offering of sickly and obviously undesirable victims.

There are many aspects of the present condition of man that seem to me alarming, but the immediate danger of genetic deterioration is not one of them. We are constantly learning more and more about human heredity. It is one of the most rapidly advancing fields of biological science. We have learned a great deal, especially, about the inheritance of physical defects, and there are already a few clinics in the country where worried couples can get useful advice about the probability of passing such defects on to their children.

The studies of such defects, and the studies of the endless hereditary peculiarities of human blood, are most interesting not for this immediate practical significance, but for the insight that is thus gained on the general nature of human heredity. For a long time the study of man seemed fairly hopeless because of the difficulty of arranging and carrying out decisive experiments. While we can't experiment with man as we can with fruit flies, we are coming to find that this difficulty is counterbalanced by a host of special advantages—especially our detailed knowledge of human populations, much greater than for any other animal. We have, in many situations, experiments neatly arranged for us, as in the case of twins, and with proper care we can gain an immense amount of knowledge from them.

Man has learned a great deal about himself and can learn a great deal more. The need for study is clear and urgent. About the need for action, I am not so sure.

But no matter from what angle we view the population question, the value of study is apparent. Perhaps the best way of rounding out this book will be to look, in the next chapter, at the various ways in which populations are studied and, in the final chapter, at the possibilities of action.

CHAPTER *15* THE STUDY OF POPULATIONS

The study of populations, in one way, is very old indeed—about as old as the development of writing. A plausible theory of the development of writing is that it arose out of the necessity of keeping records as a consequence of the increasing complexity of human affairs during the "urban revolution," a response to the needs of people aggregated into cities with their affairs controlled by continuing priestly governments.

As Gordon Childe has written:

A Sumerian temple disposed . . . of vast estates, flocks and herds, and of huge revenues. It expended and augmented that wealth by assisting its votaries with advances and loans. Now the priests who administered that revenue must give an account to their divine master of their dealings with his property and must ensure the conservation and enrichment of his estates. . . . To keep track of the god's dues and of his transactions the priest dare not rely

218

on his memory. Nor would private mnemonic devices, like tying
a knot in a handkerchief, help.

The record must be kept in such a way that it would be intel-
ligible not only to the individual making it, but to his colleagues,
and to his successors when he died.

The earliest examples of writing to survive, in Sumer, Egypt
and Crete, are mostly of this sort, inventories, records of tribute,
and suchlike memoranda of administrative transactions. Inventories of people would be just as important as inventories
of sheep, goats and jars of wheat; and an inventory of people
is a census, the basis of population study.

Our word, census, comes directly from the Latin word used
for the inventory taken at five-year intervals of persons and
property at Rome. The Roman census was started in pre-
republican days and was extended by Augustus to cover the
whole of the empire. Unfortunately, only fragments of the
records survived the breakup of the empire. The administrative practice of taking a census disappeared in medieval Europe,
with isolated exceptions like Charlemagne's Breviary and the
Domesday Book compiled for William the Conqueror. Elaborate statistical surveys were carried out by the various central
governments of China, and they were among the marvels reported by Marco Polo.

The purpose of the census, of course, was practical—to calculate taxes, raise armies, assess the numbers of people as one
variety of property of the prince or the god. The census was
thus never popular with the people being counted, and an
antipathy developed that has extended down into modern times.
When a national census was first proposed in the British House
of Commons, in 1753, the majority spokesman was moved
to shout: "I did not believe that there was any set of men or
indeed any individual of the human species, so presumptuous
and so abandoned as to make the proposal we have just heard.

. . . I hold this project to be totally subversive to the last remains of English liberty."

It was not possible to get a census bill for Great Britain through the House of Commons until 1801. The first of the modern censuses in the Western world were in colonies, in New France (Quebec) and Acadia (Nova Scotia), in 1665. A census was instituted in Iceland in 1703 and in Sweden in 1748, and in various other European states in the course of the century.

The constitution of the United States contained provision for a regular census as a means of apportioning representatives and direct taxes among the several states, and the first enumeration took place in 1790. The population at that time was counted in two main classes as slaves and free; the free were classed as whites and others; the free whites as males and females; and the free white males as under or above sixteen years of age. Further refinements were introduced with each succeeding census, leading up to the very complex statistical assessment of the state of the population of the nation that is now carried out at ten-year intervals.

The censuses of modern times, like those of ancient times, have been arranged primarily for political or fiscal purposes. But they also provide abundant material for the student of man, and scholarly statistical studies have developed in parallel with the development of the census itself. The problem of disentangling the practical and the theoretical here, as in so many phases of the development of science, is difficult and perhaps even meaningless.

We can sense the complications in the word "statistics" itself, which originally covered the collection of data of all sorts of direct and practical interest to the state. From this origin, it has grown to form a special branch of mathematics concerned with the collection and manipulation of large masses of numerical data of whatever kind, providing techniques for all of the sciences and, at the same time, building up a structure of theories and concepts of its own.

Statistics have now come to permeate not only every aspect of science, but almost every aspect of our daily lives. We face them constantly in newspapers and magazines; and we are all aware that they can be misused, as well as used, misinterpreted as well as interpreted, to "prove" almost any kind of a proposition. The study of statistics, unfortunately, has got tacked onto the end of our mathematical curriculum, so that most of us remain ignorant of its theories and concepts. Because of the importance of statistics in the modern world, many educators believe that their study should be started in high school, or at least with the freshman year in college.

It is certainly impossible to disentangle the study of population from statistics, and my efforts to avoid statistical topics in this book are probably unfortunate, to put it mildly. Statistics are there, behind all of the ideas and descriptions, and we ought to face them boldly and learn to master them.

F. Le Gros Clark has expressed this well, I think, in his discussion of "The Malthusian Heritage" in a recent book:

> The truth is that our recent mastery of global statistics has tended to go to our heads; and until we become acclimatized to living in a statistically comprehensible world, we shall continue to suffer from a kind of nervous strain. We can never again be ignorant. A mass of global statistics, slowly collected and refined over the last half-century, has suddenly transformed our outlook upon the world. The revolutionary nature of this change has not as yet been realized.

There the figures are, in each succeeding edition of *The World Almanac,* on countless desks across the land—in the flood of publications of the census bureaus of the governments of the world, in the summaries and reports of the United Nations, in the special periodicals and textbooks and research monographs. Millions, billions, rates per thousand or per hundred thousand, trends, peaks, means, modes, deviations—the stuff that describes the present state of man, that shows the recent changes, and that by projection is often boldly used to probe the future.

This is the solid frame upon which all population study must be built. Unfortunately the collection of statistics, and especially the worship of statistics, as carried out today, is primarily a phenomenon of the Western world; but a large proportion of the people of the world live in places where they can't be caught directly in the net of Western statistics. Then various sorts of "sampling" methods must be used with results that can sometimes be calculated in terms of probabilities, but that sometime also must be kept well within the category of sheer guesses. But our statistics are still the frame, the solid, basic structure to which even our wildest guess about the remote in time or place must be related.

The statistics remain a frame which, by itself, is meaningless —a gaunt skeleton. The life and meaning of these birth rates, death rates, densities and trends depends on many other sorts of study using many sorts of methods. The study of human populations, it seems to me, cannot be separated from the general study of man. Which, indeed, gets us into difficulties.

Can we have a science of man? According to the dictionary, we have one under the Greek label of anthropology. But when I look over the organization of a university, I find all sorts of other Greek and Latin labels that apply also to the scientific study of man—psychology, sociology, economics, geography. None of these departments will admit to being a mere branch of anthropology. And we can't get very far with even the "scientific" study of man without becoming entangled with the departments of history, literature, fine arts and the like. The phenomenon of the interrelatedness of things comes up again and makes all of these departments and compartments look rather odd. Yet we have got to have some sort of an organization for our facts, theories and ideas—the human mind being what it is.

I have long been puzzled by the way we organize our knowledge and our scholarly activities. The system makes very little sense when we try to examine it rationally with some given set of premises or criteria; it is understandable only when we examine it historically and look at the origins and growth of each of the separate sciences. This applies as much to physics, chemistry, astronomy, geology and biology as it does to the sciences concerned with man.

For a while, I thought I could explain the differences among the various sciences by sorting them into groups depending on whether they were characterized primarily by the nature of their subject matter, of their point of view, or of their methods. Statistics, by this system, would be an example of a science definable in terms of method; geography would be a point-of-view science (looking at things in terms of spatial relations); linguistics might be called a subject-matter science, dealing with language.

This seemed like a good idea in theory, but it failed to work when I tried to sort a collection of generally recognized "sciences" into one or another of the three categories. Most sciences have something of each. Anthropology, for instance, has a well-defined, though large, subject matter—man; it also has characteristic techniques, especially the description of customs and ways of life and the collection of stories and interpretations from informants; its point of view takes in the culture as a whole, and the individual is interesting chiefly as a specimen of the culture.

The point of view of psychology, on the other hand, leads that science to focus more on the individual and on the explanation of his peculiarities in relation to the characteristics of other individuals in similar or different circumstances. The subject matter—man—is the same, but the points of view and techniques may be quite different.

But how misleading it is to generalize like that! Both anthropology and psychology have grown, diversified, proliferated, until it is really impossible to characterize either. I remember once sitting in a conference of anthropologists, listening to their talks and discussions, and thinking that the only common denominator of the people in the room was the fact that they called themselves anthropologists. There were physical anthropologists, interested in getting measurements, in describing the variability of human populations, and in finding ways of classifying and ordering racial diversity. There were archeologists, interested in digging up and reconstructing the past; some of these would be hard to distinguish from historians, or classicists, or students of the fine arts. There were social anthropologists . . .

The distinction between social anthropology and social psychology continues to escape me—and the difference is still further blurred by the presence of a third science, sociology. Once it seemed easy: the anthropologists were concerned with the remote and the primitive; the psychologists and sociologists with the phenomena of our own culture, of Western civilization. But nowadays, anthropologists have taken to studying Hollywood and Newburyport, and social psychologists have taken to getting the peoples of the South Seas to give them their interpretations of ink blots, so this nice geographical distinction fails to hold.

Harvard has given up trying to maintain the distinctions and has united these socially-minded people in a Department of Social Relations; Yale has tried to get them all to work together in an Institute of Human Relations; and universities all over the country have tried various sorts of cross-departmental appointments, interdepartmental teaching arrangements and interdepartmental conferences and seminars. It isn't just me that's confused.

Yet there are differences, intangible and difficult to define, but nonetheless real. The sciences that now form separate departments in our great universities have had different histories, and the similarities that seem so striking today are mostly the result of growth that has become convergent. Anthropology, for instance, grew out of the natural history of the early nineteenth century; while psychology grew out of the preoccupations of philosophy. And it seems to me that one can still detect in these different sciences the long shadows of some of the early personalities influential in their development.

The points of view, the methods of study employed, and the particular subject matters that receive most emphasis, are thus still different enough. The concepts, the theories and, above all, the vocabularies are also different. Each has its own textbooks, societies and meetings, journals. These things all serve to create barriers, and the common denominator of interest in the explanation and understanding of human behavior is sometimes hard to find.

I am very conscious of these difficulties and differences as a consequence of this present foray into the area of human population study. The ramifications seem endless and carry the student into the most remote corners of human knowledge where he finds himself lost among words, ideas and methods that are strange to him. The result—this book—is almost bound to be unsatisfactory—to appear, from the standpoint of any specialty, naïve at best and downright misleading at worst.

Beyond the special case, I think it is high time we fought our way out of the compartments, the "disciplines," that history has given us, to try to find more rational criteria for specialization and study. This, to be sure, would be but a temporary expedient, since any new division will presently freeze and become outdated and inadequate; but think what fun we could have before the lines have time to become frozen again!

The study of human populations is a good example of the sort of specialization that cuts right across a whole series of traditional "disciplines," using bits of information from all of them for its particular purpose. Insofar as all organisms occur in populations, population study even crosses the division between the social sciences and the biological sciences, and observations on other animals may be useful or necessary in interpreting observations on man—and vice versa. As a matter of fact, the exchange has mostly been vice versa, because we know more about the numbers of men than about those of any other animal, and a great many of the ideas useful in general population study have come from students primarily interested in the human situation.

In our present vocabulary of specialization, the study of populations is called demography. The word was invented in 1855 by a French statistician named Achille Guillard. It is a useful word, particularly as an adjective in the case of things like the *Demographic Yearbook;* but I think we lose rather than gain if we try to make demography a formal label for a special science of population study. We get caught in the process of classification and description. We tend to make our science, demography, a branch of something else, usually sociology, so that we can fit it into a university department. We begin to worry about methods, and almost inevitably the statistical method, so exceedingly useful, comes to dominate. We have a powerful analytic tool, but in managing this tool it is hard to keep in mind large areas of human behavior relevant to population change that are hardly susceptible to statistical analysis.

Yet the human mind can't manage ideas and data without classifying them and organizing them: and the field of population study turns out to be large and complex. A tremendous amount has been written about it. I stopped writing this long enough, just now, to check through the cards under the heading "population" in the card file of the university library. I found 119 more or less general books on the subject of population— which makes me feel very sheepish about adding to the number.

But these general books are only a small fraction of the writing on the subject. The Population Association of America —a society of several hundred scholars actively involved in population study—publishes a quarterly review called *Population Index,* which includes abstracts of articles, pamphlets and books of population interest. Something over 2,000 of these are noticed every year in this index. I find that during the five years in which I have been gathering the material of this book—1949 through 1953—10,774 publications on the subject were abstracted in *Population Index!*

Of course, the statistics on publication in any field of science are staggering. The growth of human population that we have been dealing with in this book seems a slow and sedate affair compared with the growth of scientific publication. Someone has calculated that there are now almost 20,000 different journals published in the world in the field of biological sciences alone, each one with a dozen or so more or less scholarly articles every month or every quarter. The physical sciences must have a similar flood. I have seen no statistics for the social sciences, but since social scientists perhaps tend to be even wordier than biologists, I would expect an even larger flood of publications.

I occasionally find myself a member of some committee or other formed to look for a solution to this problem of publication growth. The idea of birth control, of suppression of writing (or at least of publication) never comes up, because we are dedicated to the idea of an ever-expanding science. American universities turn out more than 3,000 new Ph.D.'s every year who presumably are going to keep right on producing scholarly articles for the rest of their lives—it's their job, the way they get promotion and recognition, the way they communicate the results of their research work. The problem is, not how to cut down the publication, but how to find space to store it in our libraries, and how to find ways of indexing and abstracting, so that the particular bits of information, particular ideas, can be separated from the whole vast flood. The conversation, at such committee meetings, then turns on ways of microfilming or storing the information, and ways of devising electronic machines and indexing gadgets that will sort out the information.

These 10,774 publications on population during the last five years, then, in no way indicate that this is an unusual field of science. In fact it is a comparatively small and circumscribed area of study, with the literature particularly well indexed, thanks to the zeal and ability of the editors of *Population Index.*

A considerable proportion of these publications on population are statistical reports of various governments. I have been leafing through the last issue of the *Index,* and I notice that item number 1764 for the year 1953 is a report by the U.S. Bureau of the Census on the United States Census of Housing in five volumes. Volume I (7 books, separately bound) reports on "General Characteristics," Vol. II (5 books, separately bound) on "Nonfarm Housing Characteristics," and so on. The next item in this issue covers four volumes of the report of the 1950 census of the United States. There are similar thick official reports noticed from governments all over the world—the monthly bulletin of statistics for Thailand, the statistical yearbook of Macau, the annual report of the registrar general of Kenya. My eye is caught by Vol. IX of the report of the 1946 census of Ireland, which is entitled "Fertility of Marriage" and has 248 pages of data on numbers of children per marriage in Ireland, classified according to length of marriage, place of residence, age at marriage, religion of mother, and the like. I should have looked that up for data bearing on my discussion of Ireland in this book.

This immense accumulation of statistics from the governments of the world is the raw material of population study. It has to be summarized, analyzed, interpreted, evaluated in many different ways for many different purposes. Many interpretive studies are carried out in the census and statistical offices of the governments themselves, but most, probably, are carried out by scholars working privately—usually scholars associated with the universities of the world. Several universities have special institutes devoted to the study of population. In the United States, the Scripps Foundation for Research in Population Problems, at Miami University in Oxford, Ohio, and the Office of Population Research at Princeton University are particularly notable.

A good many of the interpretive and evaluative studies are of direct practical interest. The whole machinery of modern civilization depends on the collection and evaluation of statistics for every sort of measurable activity, including population activity. How could we manage either government or business without this background of organized facts?

There is not only the problem of describing the present, there is also the need for predicting the future. Here we run into all sorts of difficulties. The demographers would like to be able to predict the future after the fashion of the astronomers, to be able to say with some confidence that the population of the United States, or of India, or the world, would be such-and-such in the year 1975, 2000, or 2500. Clearly, however, there are too many uncertainties for precise prediction of this sort. One can only say that *if* the present trend in birth rates and death rates persists, the population will be such-and-such; *if* the trends change in certain ways, the population will be so-and-so. Uncertain as this sounds, it still has great usefulness as a guide in planning.

The more short-range the predictions, the more certain and directly useful they become. We know the number of babies that were born in 1950, and we can be quite sure that we shall have the problem of handling them in kindergarten in 1955 and in high school later. We can similarly measure the sorts of problems that will be created by the numbers of people over 70 years old in 1960. Growth trends of particular towns and cities can be predicted with reasonable accuracy for short ranges, and such predictions are a necessary basis for the planning of services of all sorts.

The whole life insurance business is based on demographic prediction, on the calculation of life expectancies under all sorts of circumstances. And as the concepts of social security and old-age pensions become more firmly established in our culture, the need for careful demographic study and prediction will increase. I have neglected these practical aspects of population study in this book, partly because they were somewhat aside from my main, descriptive purpose; partly because it is difficult to deal with them without discussing the various refinements of statistical methods that are the everyday tools of the demographers.

I have also neglected another aspect of population study— its relation to the whole field we have come to call "conservation." The resource question is clearly bound up with the past and future course of human population development and it is impossible to disentangle the two. Students of conservation, then, must necessarily also be students of population—and vice versa. I have touched on this, particularly in the matter of the means of subsistence, but in a tangential sort of way. I should, as a biologist, have pointed out more explicitly the way man—with all of his culture—is still caught in the system of the biosphere. The problems of man's relations with the rest of nature have been described well enough and often enough, but they can stand reiteration.

In one sense, this, too, is beside the point of this book. Discussion of conservation and resource relations almost inevitably gets involved with the problems of the future, which I have tried to avoid. In another sense, however, these relations are very pertinent to the topic of this book, insofar as I have been trying to probe the ways in which human population acts as a biological system, and the ways in which the usual biological concepts become inoperative or modified when man is the subject of study. There is, I think, need for more examination of the whole conservation problem in cultural terms. A historical and cross-cultural survey of man's relations with the natural environment might indeed be very interesting—but that would be another book.

Our concern in this present book has chiefly been not with the important and practical aspects of contemporary demography, nor with the problems of resource use and conservation, but with a third aspect of population study—population theory. This looks pretentious when I write it out, and I can't honestly say that I have been consciously dealing with theory. But I have been groping towards some sort of an understanding of human population behavior, and I suppose that really means toward a theory of population behavior.

The development of theories—of ideas or concepts, if you will—is certainly an important aspect of population study. Malthus, after all, was proposing and supporting a theory: that populations tend to live up to the means of subsistence with consequent vice and misery, with the corollary that escape might be possible through moral restraint. This is oversimplifying again, but I tried to describe the Malthusian theories more fully earlier in the book, though not giving sufficient attention to the many ramifications of the Malthusian ideas.

Malthus really is the starting point of a whole vast literature of population theory. Is human population governed by natural laws, or social laws, or cultural laws, or laws of any sort? Is there, in other words, any neat set of relationships that will serve to describe and predict population growth? Biologists have been particularly enamored of the idea that there must be some general law of population, some way of reducing the chaos of observations to an orderly, mathematical statement.

The immediate reaction to the theories of Malthus was a series of theories implying some sort of automatic control within the human population system—that people reproduced at a slower rate as they became more crowded, or as they engaged in more intellectual work, or as they got more and better food. The recent book by Josue de Castro purporting to show that a high reproduction rate in man is a result of inadequate diet seems to be a new statement of a theory advanced by Thomas Doubleday in 1847, in a book entitled *The True Law of Population Shewn to Be Connected with the Food of the People*.

The search for a mathematical expression of population law also started soon after Malthus—with, in fact, a Belgian astronomer and statistician, Quételet, who was a contemporary of Malthus and who was inspired to start looking into the matter by reading a French translation of the *Essay*. Quételet and another Belgian, Verhulst, worked out a very elegant formula for describing population growth, which was forgotten until two American statisticians, Raymond Pearl and Lowell Reed, arrived at the same sort of theory almost a hundred years later.

I want to avoid the mathematics of this theory (I get lost very quickly myself when a few mathematical equations enter into the discussion). Essentially, however, these students found that the most diverse population situations showed an essentially similar behavior in that a slow beginning growth would increase rapidly (the old geometric ratio) and then start to fall off, so that if plotted as a graph, the growth would be a sort of S-shaped curve. Fruit flies in a bottle, minnows in an aquarium, showed this sort of population growth; and the population of the United States showed the first half of the curve—implying that through the operation of some "natural law" the growth curve for the United States would presently begin to flatten out, like that of the fruit flies in the jar.

This business of the mathematics of population growth can be extremely fascinating, and has important implications both for biology and human demography. I suspect that the most immediate implications are biological, since relations between prey and predator, animal and food supply, can be described in terms of laboratory models and then tested by observations on what happens in nature, in meadows or ponds.

The human situation, too, may be simple enough for description in mathematical terms; but the description tells us little about the opposing forces that through their interaction produce this simplicity. The population growth of the United States may fit a smooth curve that can be described with a mathematical formula. This is like what happens when you put some fruit flies in a jar with a large supply of bananas. This perhaps means that the result of the interaction of forces within the jar and within the United States are similar, but it tells us little about the nature of the forces; to me, it is of little help in "understanding" the situation.

For "understanding" I want to look at European culture in the seventeenth century, and American Indian culture, which led the one to displace the other. The displacement, though, is hard to explain in purely cultural terms—smallpox, measles and tuberculosis, and their histories in the two populations played a part. Then, given the nature of European culture and the nature of the resources of the American continent and the biological background of human reproductive and death rates, the population growth becomes a resultant. But politics impinge on the curve, too, as events in Europe push people out, as government policy in the United States welcomes and then restricts immigration. Medicine influences the death rates; the discovery of the vulcanization process for rubber finds repercussion in the birth rates. The birth rates in particular are influenced not only by discoveries in contraception, but by changing cultural attitudes and by changing economic conditions which, at one time, may lead to a small-family pattern; which, in our present time, may be leading to a pattern of larger families.

Sir Alexander Carr-Saunders, observing how these varying cultural attitudes have influenced population over history, suggests that they may operate in such a way as to produce an "optimum" density of population for the varying cultural and economic circumstances. This brings up the very difficult question of the meaning of "optimum"—what is the "best" density for human population under any particular set of circumstances? Perhaps, for a long time, impersonal cultural and biological forces have, in general, tended to result in adjustments that have, over-all, been favorable for the survival and development of man. But the self-conscious study of man is now one of the cultural forces. "Science" has to be represented in the equation—not only science as medicine, but science as demography and sociology and anthropology, perhaps even as political science and certainly as economics. I wonder whether impersonal cultural forces are giving way to self-conscious cultural development, or whether cultural development can be self-conscious and guided.

Population theory has got us back into the net of interrelations. I'd like to end this book with an attempt, feeble and bold, to peer into the mist of this general question of the relation of science and human affairs.

CHAPTER *16* SCIENCE AND HUMAN AFFAIRS

We have been trying to look at human populations from the points of view of the various sciences that have been concerned with such matters. I can't say that the treatment has been scientific—it would be better called an unscientific look at some of the materials of science. It is unscientific because I have been unable to be thorough and objective, because I have not always tried to filter out opinion and prejudice, and because I have not cluttered up the text by citing chapter and verse for all of the sources of materials.

Or *is* it unscientific? I have been trying to be readable, and maybe I am still a victim of the feeling that to be scientific is to be dull and unreadable, so that my very effort in this book is a violation of the canons of science. This belief that to be readable is to be unscientific is probably just a superstition, though one that is widely enough held. There is nothing in the nature of science, so far as I can see, that says it must be dull. But what is the nature of science, anyway?

This is the sort of question that can be dealt with at many levels, from the surface of banter to the depths of philosophy. It is the sort of question that comes up in the most earnest of university seminars. It also sometimes comes up at faculty cocktail parties where, after a few martinis, the professors of literature sometimes needle their colleagues in chemistry—or vice versa. I want to deal with it here at the cocktail party level.

I have been practicing at this level lately. The most complicated subjects tend to seem either clear and easy—or completely unimportant—after a few martinis. Science, under these circumstances, seems very clear to me. I have worked out a standard gambit. "Science," I will say in my most serious and thoughtful manner, "is the characteristic art form of contemporary Western civilization." This, at a mixed faculty party, will start an argument going that will last until the host runs out of liquor.

The curious thing is that I half-believe my statement, even when I am cold sober. Anyone trying to develop it will soon get entangled in a net of definitions, and it takes either alcohol or a lot of patience to cut through the snarls. One of the first hazards, for instance, is the meaning of "art"—there is a clear and desperate need for a few martinis at this point. Since I haven't got the support of either the cocktail party atmosphere, or the apparatus of scholarship, I'll have to rely on trying to evade some of the important issues.

Obviously, I am using the word "art" in a very general sense, perhaps in a sense that would cover all of man's intellectual interpretations and manipulations of natural phenomena. Here we are, men living in a natural world: a world that is puzzling, capricious, beautiful, horrible, irrational, that much of the time just doesn't make sense to our minds. Somehow these minds of ours can't accept this apparent senselessness.

We can imagine a rabbit accepting the universe—grass, foxes, motherhood and rabbit passion. Sometimes we say that the rabbit has no self-consciousness; sometimes we say that the rabbit can't "reason" and that therein lies the difference. When we try to track down the essence of these differences, we mostly come back to the culture concept: to the clear fact that the rabbit lacks a symbolic means of communication. Since so much of our "thinking" involves the use of symbols, of abstractions, we deduce that the rabbit can't think. Symbol, reason, thought, consciousness— I am not going to tackle any of those words here.

Somewhere back in the Pleistocene when those prehuman ancestors of ours started developing symbolic communication, the world of the human mind started to develop. The problem, perhaps from the beginning, has been the adjustment, reconciliation, adaptation, relation of this world of the mind to the external world. I suspect that this process of adjusting is what we call "understanding" and that there are as many kinds of understanding as there arc ways of making the adjustments. Since the whole symbol system is peculiar to man, this problem of adjustment is perhaps peculiar to man, preventing him from accepting the universe as the rabbit seems to accept it.

These attempts on the part of man to interpret the external world in terms of his mental symbol systems are, then, what I would call "art," especially insofar as the interpretations lead to intellectual and emotional "satisfaction." The common denominator of our art systems is form or pattern; and when the artist finds a form that gives us a feeling of satisfaction, we have successful art. It is a matter, in the words of a title of a book by Suzanne Langer, of *Feeling and Form*.

But I had better get back to science before I am completely lost in this unfamiliar world of art in general. Science can be considered as one of the ways in which man has tried to find form and pattern in the universe, one of the ways of trying to adjust the inner world of the mind with the outer world about us. Its peculiarity lies in its methods and attitudes. These methods— controlled experimentation, precise observation, careful measurement, and the manipulation of data so obtained according to rules of logic and mathematics—lead to the development of general theories and laws, to the statement of uniformities and relationships, to the conceptual schemes that are the finished product of this art of science.

These finished products of science, these conceptual schemes, are very peculiar too, in that they are never really "finished." The theory may give great intellectual or even emotional satisfaction to its author, to other contemporary scientists, or to the contemporary world in general. But there is no feeling of permanence about the concepts: as "works of art" they are all explicitly dated. This is because, while the concepts are in one sense the "ends" of science, in another sense they are part of the means, one of the methods. The concepts, instead of being stored in a museum, are at once put to work for the purpose of aiding in further experiments and observations. And this new work almost inevitably makes it necessary to change the concepts, sometimes to scrap them altogether, as new ones are found that fit the situation of nature better.

I suppose this constant preoccupation with fitting the patterns of scientific concepts to the facts of nature is what we mean when we say science is "objective." Perhaps a subjective attitude is preoccupied more with the inner world of the mind, and an objective attitude more with the outer world of nature. I have never been able to see that the two attitudes were directly contrasting; they seem rather to be matters of degree. We can't really get away from a "subjective" element in science, because we can't get away from the mind of the observer. But we can try to minimize this personal factor as much as possible, and this attempt is another characteristic of science.

I seem to have got a long way from population in this digression on science and art—and this at the end of the book when I should be pulling things together instead of wandering off into new byways. But I want, in this last chapter, to at least glance at some of the problems of the role of science in human affairs, and especially at the relation of the scientific study of human populations to the policies of human organizations—states, nations or a world government. It seems easiest to do this by starting with glittering generalities about science in general, in the hope that presently I will be able to work down to the particular. The trouble is that it is hard to work down from glittering generalities.

I must by now have given some indication of the background of reasoning behind my proposition that "science is the characteristic art form of Western civilization." I haven't really faced the problem of defining either science or art. By trying to give art an inclusive meaning, I have spoiled the possibility of the very useful distinction among science, art, philosophy and perhaps even religion; and I'll admit that this may well be unwise.

But whether science is an art or not, I think we'll have to agree that it is characteristic of Western civilization. Not that it is unique to Western civilization—our debt to the Arabs, the Greeks, the Hindus and a whole galaxy of cultures, present and past, is clear enough. But the West has taken ideas and knowledge from all of these other cultures and developed science to a degree that has no parallel. It has created, for better or for worse, a "scientific age." And applied science has given this culture a tremendous power.

Here at the end of the book I can't get off into a discussion of how science came to be so clearly associated with the development of the West—though I think this is basic to an understanding of either science or the West. However it came about, the association is clear enough, as is also the association between science and the technology that has enabled Western culture to dominate the planet to such a large extent in modern times.

So far I have written about science as an abstract sort of thing, concerned with experiments, observations and conceptual schemes, looking at these in terms of man's attempts to understand the world about him. This is "pure" science, corresponding with the "art for art's sake" of so many artists. The arguments about pure and applied science are so similar to the arguments about pure and applied art that I find in them another support for the idea that science is really another manifestation of some general artistic impulse of the human mind.

There is no argument about the practical results of science. They are all about us and they have transformed our world. Some would regard this as an incidental, almost accidental, consequence of the development of science. At the other extreme, we have the theory that pure, or theoretical science, is really a consequence of attempts to meet practical needs. The extreme, perhaps, is reached by the Marxist ideas of economic determinism. By an extension of this, the Marxists would make everything, from physics to poetry, subservient to an essentially practical function, the needs of the state.

The question of the relationship between pure and applied science is important to us in connection with this book because its subject matter—human populations—has many immediate and practical implications. In fact, from Malthus on, most of the students of human population have clearly had practical considerations of one sort or another on their minds as the reason for carrying out their work. It is difficult to find demographers with a clearly "art for art's sake" attitude toward science. When I stop to think about this, it seems to me to be true of most social scientists, though I would be hard put to document the impression.

One exception, one avowedly impractical social science, is anthropology. Perhaps that is why I have found it so fascinating. The anthropologists have been little worried about improving society; they have simply been curious about all of the queer customs of the diverse kinds of men, and have set about collecting accounts of these customs, and trying to devise theories that would explain them. In this process they have quite incidentally, and perhaps even accidentally, made a large contribution to the "practical" study of man. They have created a storehouse of information that can be drawn on by all of the sciences, and they have achieved generalizations that affect all of the sciences concerned with man.

The greatest of the anthropological generalizations is the "culture concept." This was arrived at as an explanation of the diversity of human conduct, as a conceptual scheme that would help in giving a comprehensible pattern to the apparent chaos of the different ways of life followed by mankind. When this diversity is looked at in terms of culture—of cultural evolution, cultural diffusion, cultural adaptations—it begins to "make sense" to the observer; and he has, further, a helpful frame for the collecting of more observations on more different kinds of people.

All of this became an elaborate theory without any thought of its practical implications. Many anthropologists have become so enamored of their "science for science's sake" that they are still reluctant to face the practical consequences of their ideas. Yet it is clear that they have developed a tool that could be helpful in problems of international relations, in colonial administration, in fostering the technological development of non-Western peoples, in all of the endless human problems that involve cross-cultural relations.

If there is a basic thesis in this book of mine, it is that numbers of men, the prevalence of people, can best be understood in cultural terms. There are always the underlying biological facts of reproduction and death; but this biology, this animal nature of the human species, is shaped and modified by cultural forces in all sorts of ways. Now if we can best understand the "population problem" in cultural terms, shouldn't we look for solutions to the problem in cultural terms? But then we have moved from "pure" anthropology to "applied" anthropology, and are back again with the question of the relation between science and technology.

With a slight change in vocabulary, this could be called the question of the relationship between science and engineering. In the case of social problems, we would be dealing with social science and social engineering.

"Social engineering." There I am, caught by my culture, frightened by a couple of perfectly respectable words. My whole value system seems threatened—freedom, the importance of the individual, the inalienable rights of man, all tottering before the calculating engineer, planning society for some ultimate good. My feeling is the more absurd because social engineering is going on around us all the time, reflected in the income-tax laws, the health laws, the unemployment-relief programs, the development projects, the control of communications, and so on, in endlessly complex ways, some subtle and some obvious. The "planned economy" of the totalitarian state seems merely an extreme toward which we are all drifting with varying speeds.

My reaction to the idea of social engineering, then, is quite probably a reaction of prejudice; and any defense of the reaction may well be rationalization rather than reasoning. With this warning, I'll try to defend my position.

I suppose it derives essentially from the idea that science is an art form. As such, it would have no more inherent validity than any other art form. It would have no special claim as the one path to "truth." Indeed, if I have interpreted science correctly, it would not be concerned with truth in an absolute sense because its concepts—its theories, laws and hypotheses—are never final, absolute, but always subject to change as knowledge progresses. They are, as I have said, always dated, valid only for a particular state of knowledge.

You may say that all of this is very fine, but what about the pragmatic attitude? Science works, it gets things done, it gives us a fantastic ability to manipulate natural phenomena for our own ends. Doesn't this make it true?

I'll admit that at this point I get beyond my depth in philosophy—or perhaps the depth is a matter of semantics. There are too many different kinds of truth, too many differences in the degree to which science is successful in its operations. The absolute precision with which an astronomer can foretell an eclipse is certainly a strong argument for the truth of his theories; but the fact that the meteorologist makes such a mess of predicting the weather doesn't prove his theories to be untrue, in the same sense of truth. (There is always that "probably" in the weather prediction.)

I don't want to minimize the immense value of science as a practical tool. But I also hate to see it worshipped as the tool that can solve all of our problems. We need, I think, to steer a middle course between the fallacy of science as black magic, and the fallacy of science as white magic. Both fallacies are frighteningly prevalent in the world today.

By the fallacy of science as black magic, all of our ills are blamed on this particular art. The fallacy is held by many of our philosophers, humanists, religious leaders, who claim we have lost faith, or lost values, or lost some other vague and precious quality of our ancestors, through the spread of this insidious, materialistic, corrupting science. They forget the bloody messes created by those ancestors, without benefit of science.

By the fallacy of science as white magic, all problems can be solved by the more extensive and intensive applications of this particular art. We are living on our capital of oil and coal? Science will find a way out. The people of Java have a deplorable standard of living? Send them scientific technology. The great problems of our day are social rather than material? Channel our resources into social science, and the social problems will be solved as the material ones have been solved.

As I write this, I realize that I often tend to the faith in science as white magic—not faith in science as technology, but faith in science as art, as a way of reconciling the inner world of the mind with the external world. This surely is a personal reaction, resulting from the fact that I have found my greatest satisfactions, got my glimpses of peace and understanding, through this way of looking at things. And, in true missionary style, I want to share my satisfactions.

But we started off, a while ago, on social engineering, and on the practical relationships between social science and the population problem. I think we have to be careful here not to draw too close a parallel between the social sciences and the natural sciences: not to argue from chemistry and industry to sociology and society.

One great difficulty with social science, surely, lies in the nature of objectivity. If the basic concern of science is with adjustment or fit between the human mind and the external world, and if objectivity means emphasis on the characteristics of the external world, this objectivity becomes increasingly difficult as we move toward the study of man himself. The mind of the observer is always intruding into science; but the problem resulting from this may be quite different in the natural and social sciences. We have arrived at a chemistry that seems to work equally well in the hands of an American, a Chinese, a Russian, or an Indian; but I doubt whether this could be said for any of the social sciences. The explanation is often made that the social sciences are "still young" but this simply avoids the question. I suspect that the difference is profound.

Social engineering, then, needs to be examined in a different context from chemical engineering. Perhaps the social scientists haven't yet found the really effective basis for analysis in their sciences. The occasional social scientists who are sure that in their science lies the cure for the ills of society sometimes remind me of the alchemists, who were for so long dazzled by the will-o'-the-wisp of the transmutation of elements, of immediate practicality. The alchemists learned a great deal, furnished a substratum of knowledge and methods on which modern chemistry was eventually built—but only after the objectives had been changed. Chemistry, curiously, found out about the transmutation of some elements—when it was no longer trying.

I am impressed by the insights we have already obtained from social science, and I have a great faith in its future possibilities, in the usefulness of turning scientific techniques inward to look at the problems of man himself. The faith, however, is mostly in the possibility of thus continuing to increase our understanding of man and his nature. Out of such understanding, solutions to problems will surely emerge—but not necessarily through the efforts of the scientists alone in some engineering operation.

I doubt whether my friends in anthropology, sociology, psychology or economics could do a better job, now, of guiding society than my friends in law, politics or business. In fact, we might regard law, politics, business and the like as the fields of applied social science. In these fields of action, then, the insights of the scientist could be blended with, and balanced against, the insights of other sorts of observers of the human scene, to arrive at rational developments for the greatest "good." This, surely, is what is actually happening. But the pace sometimes seems disastrously slow.

The problem, then, is not only one of continuing the development of social research, but of communicating the results of this research to all sectors of society and especially to the action groups. I think the ivory-tower complex, the isolating wall of jargon, is unfortunate in any science, but particularly unfortunate in social science. Perhaps it would be better not to think of the application of social science in terms of social engineering, but in terms of communication between the scientist and other parts of society—a communication that must be two-way insofar as solutions to the practical problems of mankind are concerned. The solutions must always be acceptable to the culture if they are to work. If they are not acceptable and if the problem is to be solved or eased, either the solution or the culture must change—clearly a matter of interaction.

So with the "population problem." I can't see any question about the reality of the problem. The whole system of nature bears witness to the need for adjustment between natality and mortality, between the rate at which young are produced and the hazards of death for that particular kind of organism. The birth rates of elephants are in accord with the hazards of elephant existence, of chipmunks with the hazards of chipmunk existence. The adjustment is not precise—if it were, organic nature would be an unchanging, precisely adjusted machine. Populations fluctuate over years and over geologic eras; sometimes new populations appear and spread; sometimes old populations become extinct. The relative constancy, the changes and the adjustments are all part of the grand pattern of organic evolution.

Man, too, is a product of organic evolution. That he survived and multiplied is proof that his birth rates were adapted to the hazards of his existence through that long period of Pleistocene evolution. But with the beginning and accelerating development of cultural evolution, man's relations with his environment began undergoing drastic changes. The cultural changes affected human ecology rather than human physiology, which remains purely a product of the slow process of organic evolution. But the ecological changes had a profound influence on man's population adjustments.

I have tried, in this book, to outline the major aspects of these ecological changes. The end result has been a very great change in the hazards of existence. It seems to me axiomatic that if these changes in the hazards of existence are to remain, and if the human species is to survive, there must also be changes in the birth rate. Since we are dealing with ecological relations affected by cultural evolution, it seems to me also to follow that the adjustments must be cultural.

We have evidence enough that these cultural adjustments do

occur. It has probably been a very long time since the birth rate of any human population has been a product of purely biological factors, and there is evidence from many cultures of the development of practices more or less deliberately aimed at lowering birth rates. The birth-death adjustment has become most conspicuously out of balance in the nations of the modern West as these nations have gained increasing control over the ecological causes of death. Here, too, there is plenty of evidence of a compensating change in birth rates. It is difficult to assess how much this has been the result of the deliberate propaganda of birth control agencies, and how much the product of indirect pressures, such as the felt need of a family to give better education to fewer children.

This makes it look as though the "problem" might solve itself. This seems perfectly possible within Western culture, though there is considerable question as to how rapidly the problem will solve itself—as to the urgency of trying to promote wider diffusion of birth control knowledge. The clearest case for urgency, however, is when we look at the problem from a cross-cultural point of view. We have rightly tried to share the Western techniques of controlling ecological death with all of the other peoples of the planet. Doesn't this carry with it a corresponding need for sharing our knowledge of techniques for the ecological control of birth?

While this manuscript was in its final stages, a book appeared written by Harrison Brown, called *The Challenge of Man's Future*. Reading this, I had a horrid feeling that Mr. Brown had already written my book for me, so that I might as well abandon the manuscript. But they are different books, so I went ahead with my writing. Mr. Brown is primarily looking to the future, while I have been trying to understand how we arrived at the present. Mr. Brown has given a broad and penetrating analysis of man's relations with his resources—past, present and future— which I have brushed aside in this book in order to look more narrowly at the questions of population. But Mr. Brown's book, in total effect, is a persuasive statement of the importance and urgency of the population problem—of the need for social action. He is dealing boldly with the problems that I have only touched on here at the end of my book.

Mr. Brown's look at the future is not very reassuring. Judging from present trends, there is great likelihood that the world will again become involved in total war. Such war may well be disastrous, not only in terms of immediate damage, but in terms of the possibility of recovery. Industrial economy may well not be able to survive a war of the destructiveness now possible, and in that case, peoples everywhere might be reduced to the old levels of agrarian economy, with the Malthusian propositions governing their populations.

If we escape war, we may well drift into a totalitarian sort of world organization for human society. We can see about us everywhere the increasing complexity of organization required by the increasing numbers of people and the increasing specialization, skill and power required for the exploitation, utilization and distribution of resources. If war doesn't get us, we may fall victim to my pet bugaboo, social engineering. There hardly seems any escape from the internationally planned economy, from the sort of thing pictured for us by George Orwell in *1984,* or by Aldous Huxley in his *Brave New World.*

There must be a way out. Mr. Brown doesn't picture it very clearly; I have no blueprints for escape. Science as science can't give us the answer. Science, as one of the humanities, surely can help, giving us facts, impressions, understandings and techniques with which we can build. But it is only one of the arts that will serve man to meet the challenge of his future.

I revert, I suppose, to the sort of faith that gave Rousseau and Condorcet their confidence in the perfectibility of man. Malthus showed, very logically, the fallacy of their reasoning—he was a scientist and a realist. The Malthusian argument now would have to be rewritten in quite different terms, because we have accumulated a great deal of information since his day, even though our ignorance is still more impressive than our knowledge. The arguments of the French philosophers would also have to be rewritten, and expressed in different terms.

I suppose I would express the argument not so much in terms of the perfectibility of man, as in terms of the improvability of culture. If anything is clear from history and anthropology, it is the great plasticity of culture. It has changed, sometimes with surprising rapidity; and in terms of our values of individual freedom, of the right to health and happiness for the greatest possible number, the over-all changes, particularly in the West, have surely been towards improvement.

For the world as a whole, or for any large part of it, we are far from any ideal. And when we try to calculate the future, the ideal seems impossibly remote. But man and this culture of his are curious phenomena—with the equipment we have, essentially unpredictable. In this uncertainty I find my hope.

NOTES

The reference list for a book like the present one should serve two rather different purposes. On the one hand, it should indicate to scholars the sources of my information and misinformation; and on the other hand, it should help any reader who may want to explore some particular topic more fully. Fortunately, many of my references will serve both purposes, since I have depended quite largely on garnering ideas and information from general books. I feel no competence, however, for drawing up a recommended reading list because the literature on the various topics covered in the book is vast, and I may well have overlooked the most valuable and pertinent items.

Since detailed and scholarly bibliography would be out of place, I have tried to limit documentation as much as possible. In particular, I have avoided citing journal articles except to indicate the sources of direct quotes or of unusual information. Mostly, as must be clear enough from the text, I have depended on secondary sources.

I have frequently consulted general reference books—encyclopedias, several successive editions of the *World Almanac*

251

and the *Demographic Yearbook* of the United Nations. In such cases, I have made no specific reference to the source of information. In the final stages of the manuscript, I made use of the store of data assembled by Woytinsky and Woytinsky (1953). Two population textbooks have been on my desk at all times: Landis (1943) and Thompson (the 1953 edition, during the last year of writing). I have not surveyed the various other texts to form an opinion as to whether these were the "best." I have had, however, a continuing admiration for Thompson's writings—his textbook as well as his other writings—and I am sure that he would be a reliable guide for any reader wishing to start out to explore demography.

The first book that I read on population was the 1922 volume by Sir Alexander Carr-Saunders—*The Population Problem; A Study in Human Evolution*—and it probably remains the strongest influence on my thinking. I also clearly owe a considerable debt to various recent books on population, especially Vogt (1948), Osborn (1948) and Brown (1954), though I think my approach is different from that of any of these. I particularly liked the book by Harrison Brown, and the reading list he provides is a better guide for exploration of the population literature than anything I could hope to work out.

In general, where there is a clear indication of my sources in the text, I have not repeated the citation in these notes, but have listed the reference directly in the bibliography. Several books of primarily historic interest that were mentioned in the text have not been listed with the references, as this would seem mere pedantry.

CHAPTER 2. THE NUMBERS OF MEN

The estimates on wild rodents are from Sanderson (1951); he includes only a limited amount of information on the abundance of mammals in his book. The best introduction to population studies of mammals—and the natural history of mammals in general—is Bourlière (1954). David Davis has summarized his rat studies in a paper published in 1953. The quotation comparing the difficulty of making population studies in Africa with studies of adultery in England is from the preface to Kuczynski (1948). The figures on races, religions and languages were garnered from Woytinsky and Woytinsky (1953). My summary of the Willcox estimates of modern population growth is based entirely on the material in Carr-Saunders (1936). The figures on French Canadians were derived from Fawcett (1947). Statistics on Roman populations, based on Eduard Meyer, *Die Bevölkerung des Altertums,* are given by Woytinsky and Woytinsky. All quotations and statistics on medieval England are from Russell (1948). This book seems to me a fine example of the way many aspects of medieval demography can be revealed by careful detective work. The more general study by Homans (1942) also has a great deal of information bearing on population in medieval England. My discussion of the Mooney estimates of the populations of American Indians is based entirely on Kroeber (1939).

CHAPTER 3. THE NATURE OF MAN

I can't document this mixture of biology and anthropology; I can only recommend books for further reading. This will perhaps also serve to give an indication of my own background reading. I think the best introduction to biological evolution for the general reader is Simpson (1953). His earlier book, (Simpson, 1949), deals more explicitly with human evolution and the special problems of its meaning for man. For a book on fossil man, my first recommendation is Howells (1944); for the geological background of the Pleistocene, Flint (1947). My general concepts of social or cultural evolution are largely derived from Gordon Childe, especially his 1941 and 1951 books. Kluckhohn (1949) has written a nontechnical account of the strategy of social anthropology and of the anthropological concept of culture. At a more technical level, I greatly admire Kroeber's introduction to anthropology (1948).

I ought to apologize for the title of this chapter—which is based on my inability to resist the neat sequence of numbers, nature and kinds in the chapter headings. It is misleading because of my complete neglect of the psychological approach to the problems of human nature. This relative neglect, now that I think of it, characterizes the whole book. But how could you get a really balanced approach?

CHAPTER **4.** THE KINDS OF MAN

Even a limited and judicious selection of references on the approaches of science to the study of races would add intolerably to the length of the bibliography of this book. I'll cite only Coon, Garn and Birdsell (1950). I think this represents a rather special point of view, but it has a bibliography that also covers other approaches. The detailed study of Europe by Coon (1939), mentioned in the text, shows how complicated racial study is.

Anthropology and psychology have recently found "national character" a rich field for exploration. Fortunately there is no bibliographic problem here because I need only cite the paper by Margaret Mead (1953) in *Anthropology Today*, where the literature is listed and evaluated. (This symposium volume, *Anthropology Today*, is a rich mine of information on many aspects of human study.) So far as social class is concerned, I have mentioned the work of Warner and Lunt (1941) and

Hollingshead (1949) in the text; for a general survey of the subject, perhaps the best single reference is the anthology edited by Bendix and Lipset (1953). Kiser (1942) was cited in the text in connection with the 1935 study of the relation between social class and birth rates. Anyone interested in this subject should consult the numerous more recent articles by Kiser and others in the *Milbank Memorial Fund Quarterly*. For an introduction to the study of social structure in animals, I would recommend Allee (1951) and the chapter in Bourlière (1954).

My omission of personality classification is justifiable because this has rarely been related to population. An exception is the concept of "inner-direction" and "other-direction" developed by Riesman (1950). He shows how personality changes may be associated with changing population conditions—a subject that surely warrants more exploration.

CHAPTER 5. THE MEANS OF SUBSISTENCE

Here I have mostly mentioned my sources in the text. I think the best study of Malthus, and of the background of his time, is Bonar (1924), a book that I found readable and informative. I have oversimplified in my discussion by not going into the antecedents of Malthusian thought, but this is covered in the Bonar book. It seems to me superfluous to cite particular works by Godwin, Condorcet and other proponents of the perfectibility of man. Again I refer the reader to Bonar, or to the encyclopedia articles on the various authors. Similarly, I do not include Darwin in the bibliography, though I have quoted from his autobiography. I ought, though, to include at least one reference to the general subject of the relation between Darwin and social thought. Perhaps Barzun (1947) will best serve this purpose.

For a general survey of ecology—food relations, territory, population—the standard reference is the big book by Allee and others (1949). For less technical accounts of these things, with special regard for mammals, I can again do no better than to cite Bourlière (1954).

CHAPTER **6.** HUMAN REPRODUCTION

For general physiological background, I have depended on Parkes (1952). Comparative studies on reproduction in mammals have been summarized by Asdell (1946). The remarks on human multiple births are mostly based on Scheinfeld (1950). Studies on human sexual behavior have been summarized by Ford (1945) and Ford and Beach (1951). I am clearly indebted at many points to the Kinsey reports—though the female volume was not published until much of my manuscript had been completed. I might cite Ellis (1950) as an example of work supporting my remarks about the irrelevance of race and climate to age at puberty. Ellis found no significant differences associated with either race or climate in comparative studies in Nigeria and England. My sources for information on conception in man were chiefly Dickinson and Bryant (1932) and Dickinson (1933). The data on frequency of intercourse are from Pearl (1939). Human reproductive rates are discussed in all of the demographic textbooks; Thompson (1948) gives a general review.

CHAPTER **7.** THE CONTROL OF REPRODUCTION

My main source in this chapter has been the book by Norman Himes (1936) on the history of contraception. Information about contraception, abortion and infanticide in various cultures has been reviewed by Carr-Saunders (1922) and Krzywicki (1934). Stix and Notestein (1940) have reported on a study of contraception under contemporary conditions in the United States. Valuable studies on the circumstances and prevalence of contraception have appeared in the *Milbank Memorial Fund Quarterly*. My other sources all seem to be clearly enough indicated in the text.

CHAPTER **8.** THE CAUSES OF DEATH

The statistics are mostly from various volumes of the *Demographic Yearbook*. The biological ideas about death—physiological versus ecological, and density dependent versus density independent—are set forth and fully documented in the ecology book by Allee and others (1949). Human longevity has been studied particularly by Pearl (1934), as well as by Dublin, Lotka and Spiegelman (1949).

CHAPTER **9.** MAN AGAINST MAN

My major sources are indicated in the text; I have depended especially on Wright (1942). At many points in writing this book, I have gone back to look up something or other in the various works of Edward Westermarck, and in connection with this present chapter I remember rereading the discussion of cannibalism in his *Origin and Development of Moral Ideas*. I ought to cite several Westermarck volumes in my bibliography, but I'll limit myself to this one and acknowledge here my general debt—which goes back to the book browsing of my undergraduate days. The Kroeber quote is from his 1939 book, pp. 148-149.

CHAPTER 10. FAMINE

I found the Egyptian inscription, with which the chapter starts, in the study of starvation by Ancel Keys and others. The statistics on famines also come mostly from the Keys book, except for the quotation from Thompson. There is an immense literature on famine, starvation, hunger, nutritional deficiencies and related topics. This has been surveyed by the Keys study and there seems no point in picking out a few items for inclusion in the bibliography of this book. De Castro (1952) also has a good bibliography, including the very items that would seem to me to refute his thesis. The Irish story, as I stated in the text, is based on a blend of Salaman (1949) and Connell (1950).

CHAPTER 11. DISEASE

My remarks about the history of diseases—new diseases, old diseases, changes in leprosy and plague—are in general based on Zinsser's account. Yellow fever and malaria were used as examples of parasite relations because of my direct familiarity with these diseases. I have discussed the idea of the post-Neolithic origin of our major contagions with various epidemiologists and found them interested—but evaluation is difficult in the absence of facts. The material on smallpox in America is all from Stearn and Stearn (1945) including the various historical quotes. The effect of disease in the Pacific, which I only mention, is touched on by Thompson (1946) and treated in more detail by Roberts (1927).

CHAPTER **12.** THE POSTPONEMENT OF DEATH

There are many books on the history of medicine and public health, and I have no competence to suggest which might be "best." In writing this chapter, I have drawn directly on Sigerist (1941 and 1944), Stern (1941) and Winslow (1952). My ideas about medieval sanitation and public health probably mostly come from Mumford (1938). Cities are fascinating things to study (though not, for me, to live in), and I debated including a chapter on the special aspects of city populations; but this seemed a departure from the basic organization of the book. The sketch of the history of smallpox vaccination in this chapter is based on several sources, but chiefly Connell (1950) who goes into the matter with characteristic thoroughness in relation to Irish population developments.

CHAPTER **13.** MIGRATION

The demographic textbooks all include considerable discussion of migration, especially of modern international movements of peoples. I particularly like the discussion in Thompson (1953). The demographers, however, pay little attention to the movements of primitive people; these are studied by anthropologists and are generally reviewed in their textbooks. Keith's ideas about the relative immovability of ancient man are developed in his 1949 book; this also contains a general discussion of the influence of territory on human evolution. I had thought, until I read this book, that my ideas about this were somewhat original. On the subject of the antiquity of man in America, in addition to the Solecki article, I would recommend reading Roberts (1951) and Carter (1952).

CHAPTER 14. THE IDEA OF EUGENICS

Biologists tend generally to take eugenics seriously, and I expect that many of my colleagues will raise their eyebrows at the attitude I have taken in this chapter. My good friend Robert Cook has recently written a crusading book, entitled *Human Fertility,* which has a strong eugenics flavor. I recommend this to anyone who wants an easy-to-read and accurate statement of a point of view almost opposite the one I have taken here. The explanation of the basic principles of genetics in Cook's book seems to me particularly good, but I can't see the alarming deductions that he makes about the genetic future of man. The attitude expressed by Dunn and Dobzhansky (1952) seems to me more plausible. The quotation from H. J. Muller is by way of the Dunn and Dobzhansky book (p. 14). Of the general books on eugenics, I like best that by Frederick Osborn (1940); the definition of feeble-mindedness is by way of Osborn (p. 16).

I debated including in this chapter some discussion of the experiment in eugenics carried out by ancient Sparta, but meaningful discussion of this or other aspects of population in ancient Greece would have carried us too far afield. There is an interesting discussion of the Spartan way of life, and of Greek population in relation to infanticide and colonization in Cross (1935), and a treatment from the eugenics point of view by Roper (1913).

CHAPTER 15. THE STUDY OF POPULATIONS

The quotation from Gordon Childe on the origin of writing is from the Mentor edition of his 1941 book (p. 143). The Le Gros Clark quotation is from Clark and Pirie (1951), (p. 26). The various theories of population growth are discussed at some length by Landis (1943) and Thompson (1953) and in other textbooks. Chapter III of D'Arcy Thompson's great book *On Growth and Form* contains an extended history of the mathematical treatment of population, with references to the original work of Quételet, Verhulst, Pearl and Reed and others, and should be consulted by anyone interested in the mathematical theory.

CHAPTER 16. SCIENCE AND HUMAN AFFAIRS

I can't document this chapter. The ideas have been picked up here and there over years of reading and I probably could not track down the sources if I tried. I excuse myself by thinking that references on the philosophy of science would be out of place in this book, anyway. Insofar as biology is concerned, the best analysis of its philosophy is a little book recently published by Agnes Arber, called *The Mind and the Eye*. Miss Arber includes a wide-ranging bibliography of criticism of science, art and philosophy, and her book makes a good starting point for explorations of the relations of these things.

The organizational problems presented by growing populations, emphasized by Harrison Brown, worry me as much as any aspect of the future. In this connection, I should like to call attention to the thought-provoking book by Kenneth Boulding (1953) on *The Organizational Revolution*.

REFERENCES

ALLEE, W. C.
1951. Cooperation among animals—with human implications. New York: Henry Schuman, 233 pp., 5 pls., 48 figs.

ALLEE, W. C., A. E. EMERSON, O. PARK, T. PARK and
K. P. SCHMIDT
1949. Principles of animal ecology. Philadelphia: W. B. Saunders Co., xii + 837 pp., 263 figs.

ARBER, AGNES
1954. The mind and the eye; a study of the biologist's standpoint. Cambridge: at the University Press, xi + 146 pp.

ANGEL, J. L.
1947. The length of life in ancient Greece. Journal of Gerontology, vol. 2, pp. 18-24.

ASDELL, S. A.
1946. Patterns of mammalian reproduction. Ithaca: Comstock Pub. Co., xi + 437 pp., 11 pls.

263

BARTHOLOMEW, G. A. and J. B. BIRDSELL
1953.   Ecology and the protohominids. American Anthropologist, vol. 55, pp. 481-498.

BARZUN, JACQUES
1947.   Darwin, Marx, Wagner; critique of a heritage. Boston: Little, Brown & Co., xii + 420 pp.

BENDIX, REINHARD and S. M. LIPSET (Editors)
1953.   Class, Status and power. Glencoe, Ill.: The Free Press, 725 pp.

BONAR, JAMES
1924.   Malthus and his work. London: George Allen & Unwin Ltd., vi + 438 pp., 1 ill.

BOULDING, K. E.
1953.   The organizational revolution; a study in the ethics of economic organization. New York: Harper & Bros., xxxiv + 286 pp.

BOURLIÈRE, FRANÇOIS
1954.   The natural history of mammals. New York: Alfred A. Knopf, xxi + 363 + xi pp., 121 figs.

BROWN, HARRISON
1954.   The challenge of man's future. New York: The Viking Press, xii + 290 pp., 31 figs.

CARPENTER, C. R.
1934.   A field study of the behavior and social relations of howling monkeys. Comparative Psychology Monographs, vol. 10, no. 2, 168 pp., 16 pls.

CARR-SAUNDERS, A. M.
1922.   The population problem; a study in human evolution. Oxford: The Clarendon Press, 516 pp.
1936.   World population; past growth and present trends. Oxford: The Clarendon Press, xv + 336 pp.

CARTER, G. F.
1952.   Man in America: a criticism of scientific thought. Scientific Monthly, vol. 73, pp. 297-307.

CHILDE, V. G.
1941. Man makes himself. London: Watts & Co., xiii + 242
pp., 12 figs. (Edition of "The Thinkers Library"; first
published in 1936 in "The Library of Science and Culture"; reprinted: New York: The New American Library,
192 pp., 11 figs., 1951.)
1951. Social evolution. New York: Henry Schuman, viii +
184 pp.

CLARK, F. LE GROS and N. W. PIRIE (Editors)
1951. Four thousand million mouths: scientific humanism and
the shadow of world hunger. New York: Oxford Univ.
Press, v + 222 pp., 2 figs.

CONNELL, K. H.
1950. The population of Ireland, 1750-1845. Oxford: Clarendon Press, xi + 293 pp.

COOK, R. C.
1951. Human fertility: the modern dilemma. New York: Wm.
Sloane Associates, viii + 380 pp.

COON, C. S.
1939. The races of Europe. New York: Macmillan Co., xvi +
739 pp., 46 pls.

COON, C. S., S. M. GARN and J. B. BIRDSELL
1950. Races; a study of the problems of race formation in man.
Springfield, Ill.: Charles C. Thomas, xiv + 153 pp., 15
pls.

CROSS, G. J.
1935. The triumph of Athens. Oxford: Pen-in-Hand Publ.
Co., 175 pp.

DAVIS, D. E.
1953. The characteristics of rat populations. Quarterly Review
of Biology, vol. 28, pp. 373-401, 15 figs.

DAVIS, KINGSLEY
1951. The population of India and Pakistan. Princeton: Princeton Univ. Press, xvi + 263 pp., 22 maps, 55 figs.

DE CASTRO, JOSUE
1952. The geography of hunger. Boston: Little, Brown & Co., 337 pp.

DICKINSON, R. L.
1933. Human sex anatomy. Baltimore: Williams & Wilkins Co., xiii + 145 pp., 175 pls.

DICKINSON, R. L. and L. S. BRYANT
1932. Control of conception; an illustrated medical manual. Baltimore: Williams & Wilkins Co., xii + 290 pp.

DUBLIN, L. I., A. J. LOTKA and MORTIMER SPIEGELMAN
1949. Length of life; a study of the life table. New York: Ronald Press Co., xxv + 379 pp.

DUNN, L. C. and TH. DOBZHANSKY
1952. Heredity, race and society. New York: New American Library, 143 pp.

ELLIS, R. W. B.
1950. Age of puberty in the tropics. British Medical Journal, 14 Jan., 1950, pp. 85-89. (Reprinted in the Yearbook of Physical Anthropology for 1950.)

FARRIS, E. J.
1950. Human fertility and problems of the male. White Plains, N.Y.: The Author's Press, Inc., xvi + 211 pp., 2 pls., 33 figs.

FAWCETT, C. B.
1947. The numbers and distribution of mankind. The Advancement of Science, vol. 4, pp. 140-147, 2 figs. (Reprinted in the Yearbook of Physical Anthropology for 1947.)

FIRTH, RAYMOND
1936. We, the Tikopia; a sociological study of kinship in primitive Polynesia. New York: American Book Co., xxv + 605 pp., 27 figs.

FLINT, R. F.
1947. Glacial geology and the Pleistocene epoch. New York: John Wiley & Sons, xviii + 589 pp., 6 pls., 88 figs.

FORD, C. S.
1945. A comparative study of human reproduction. Yale University Publications in Anthropology, no. 32, 33 pp.

FORD, C. S. and F. A. BEACH
1951. Patterns of sexual behavior. New York: Harper & Bros., viii + 307 pp., 16 figs.

FORDE, C. D.
1949. Habitat, economy and society; a geographical introduction to ethnology. New York: E. P. Dutton & Co., xv + 500 pp., 108 figs.

HAILEY, LORD [MALCOLM]
1938. An African survey; a study of problems arising in Africa south of the Sahara. Oxford Univ. Press, xxviii + 1837 pp., 6 maps.

HIMES, NORMAN
1936. Medical history of contraception. Baltimore: Williams & Wilkins Co., xxxi + 521 pp., 29 figs.

HOLLINGSHEAD, A. B.
1949. Elmtown's youth; the impact of social classes on adolescents. New York: John Wiley & Sons, xi + 480 pp.

HOMANS, G. C.
1942. English villagers of the thirteenth century. Cambridge: Harvard Univ. Press, xiv + 478 pp., 5 maps.

HOWELLS, WILLIAM
1944. Mankind so far. New York: Doubleday & Co., xii + 319 pp., 7 pls., 37 figs.

KEITH, SIR ARTHUR
1949. A new theory of human evolution. New York: Philosophical Library, x + 451 pp.

KEYS, ANCEL, J. BROZEK, A. HENSCHEL, O. MICKELSEN and
H. L. TAYLOR
1950. The biology of human starvation. Minneapolis: Univ.
Minnesota Press, xl + 1385 pp., 158 figs., in 2 vols.

KINSEY, ALFRED, W. B. POMEROY and C. E. MARTIN
1948. Sexual behavior in the human male. Philadelphia: W. B.
Saunders Co., xv + 804 pp., 173 figs.
1953. Sexual behavior in the human female. Philadelphia:
W. B. Saunders Co., xxx + 842 pp., 155 figs. (With P. H.
Gebhard as additional author.)

KISER, C. V.
1942. Group differences in urban fertility. Baltimore: Williams
& Wilkins Co., xii + 284 pp.

KLUCKHOHN, CLYDE
1949. Mirror for man; the relation of anthropology to modern
life. New York: Whittlesey House, xi + 313 pp.

KROEBER, A. L.
1939. Cultural and natural areas of native North America.
Berkeley: Univ. California Press, xi + 242 pp., 28 maps.
1948. Anthropology; race, language, culture, psychology, pre-
history. New York: Harcourt, Brace & Co., xii + 856 +
xxxix pp., 42 figs.

KRZYWICKI, LUDWIK
1934. Primitive society and its vital statistics. London: Macmillan & Co., xiii + 589 pp.

KUCZYNSKI, R. R.
1948. Demographic survey of the British Colonial Empire.
Vol. I, West Africa. Oxford Univ. Press, xiii + 821 pp.

LANDIS, P. H.
1943. Population problems; a cultural interpretation. New
York: Thomas Y. Crowell Co., xxi + 202 pp., ill.

LORENZ, K. Z.
1952. King Solomon's ring; new light on animal ways. New
York: Thomas Y. Crowell Co., xxi + 202 pp., ill.

MALTHUS, T. R.

1798. An essay on the principle of population, as it affects the future improvement of society, with remarks on the speculations of Mr. Godwin, M. Condorcet and other writers. London: Printed for J. Johnson, in St. Paul's Churchyard, ix + 396 pp. (Facsimile reprint, Macmillan, London, 1926, with notes by James Bonar. Of later editions, the most readily available is in "Everyman's Library" in two volumes based on the seventh edition.)

MEAD, MARGARET

1953. National character. *In* Anthropology Today, A. L. Kroeber, editor. Univ. of Chicago Press, pp. 642-667.

MUMFORD, LEWIS

1938. The culture of cities. New York: Harcourt, Brace & Co., xii + 586 pp., 32 pls.

MURIE, ADOLPH

1944. The wolves of Mount McKinley. Washington: U. S. Gov. Printing Office, xx + 238 pp., 58 figs.

OSBORN, FAIRFIELD

1948. Our plundered planet. Boston: Little, Brown & Co., xiv + 217 pp.

OSBORN, FREDERICK

1940. Preface to eugenics. New York: Harper & Bros., xi + 312 pp., 12 figs.

PARKES, A. S. (Editor)

1952. Marshall's physiology of reproduction, Vol. II, New York: Longmans, Green & Co., xx + 880 pp., 294 figs.

PEARL, RAYMOND

1934. The ancestry of the long-lived. Baltimore: Johns Hopkins Press, xiii + 168 pp.

1939. The natural history of population. New York: Oxford Univ. Press, xii + 416 pp., 40 figs.

RICHARDS, AUDREY I.

1932. Hunger and work in a savage tribe; a functional study

of nutrition among the southern Bantu. London: George Routledge & Sons, xvi + 238 pp.

RIESMAN, DAVID
1950.   The lonely crowd; a study of the changing American character. New Haven: Yale Univ. Press, xviii + 386 pp.

ROBERTS, F. H. H.
1951.   The early Americans. Scientific American, vol. 184, no. 2, pp. 15-18, ill.

ROBERTS, S. H.
1927.   Population problems of the Pacific. London: George Routledge & Sons, xx + 411 pp., 4 maps.

ROPER, A. G.
1913.   Ancient eugenics. Oxford: B. H. Blackwell, 75 pp.

ROYAL COMMISSION ON POPULATION
1949.   Report. London: H. M. Stationery Office, xii + 259 pp.

RUSSELL, J. C.
1948.   British medieval population. Albuquerque: Univ. of New Mexico Press, xvi + 389 pp.

SALAMAN, R. N.
1949.   The history and social influence of the potato. Cambridge: at the University Press, xxiv + 685 pp., 105 figs.

SANDERSON, I. T.
1951.   How to know the American mammals. New York: New American Library, 164 pp., 182 figs. (Also a hard-cover edition, Boston: Little, Brown & Co.)

SCHEINFELD, AMRAM
1950.   The new you and heredity. New York: J. B. Lippincott Co., xxii + 616 pp., ill.

SIGERIST, H. E.
1941.   Medicine and human welfare. New Haven: Yale Univ. Press, ix + 148 pp., 20 figs.
1944.   Civilization and disease. Ithaca: Cornell Univ. Press, xi + 255 pp., ill.

SIMPSON, G. G.

1949. The meaning of evolution: a study of the history of life and of its significance for man. New Haven: Yale Univ. Press, xv + 364 pp., 38 figs.

1953. Life of the past; an introduction to paleontology. New Haven: Yale Univ. Press, xii + 198 pp., 48 figs.

SOLECKI, RALPH

1951. How man came to North America. Scientific American, vol. 184, no. 1, pp. 11-15, ill.

SPENCER, SIR BALDWIN and F. J. GILLEN

1927. The Arunta; a study of a stone age people. London: Macmillan & Co., xliv + 646 pp., 247 figs., in 2 vols.

STEARN, E. W. and A. E. STEARN

1945. The effect of smallpox on the destiny of the Amerindian. Boston: Humphries, Inc., 153 pp.

STERN, B. J.

1941. Society and medical progress. Princeton: Princeton Univ. Press, xvii + 264 pp.

STIX, R. K. and F. W. NOTESTEIN

1940. Controlled fertility; an evaluation of clinic service. Baltimore: Williams & Wilkins Co., xiv + 201 pp., 16 figs.

STRACHEY, G. L.

1931. Portraits in miniature and other essays. London: Chatto & Windus, 218 pp.

THOMPSON, D'ARCY

1942. On growth and form. (2nd ed.) Cambridge: at the University Press, 1116 pp., 554 figs.

THOMPSON, WARREN

1946. Population and peace in the Pacific. Chicago: Univ. Chicago Press, 397 pp., 7 figs.

1948. Plenty of people. (rev. ed.). New York: Ronald Press Co., xiv + 281 pp., ill.

1953. Population problems. (4th ed.) New York: McGraw-Hill Book Co., xiii + 488 pp.

TINDALE, N. B.
1953. Tribal and intertribal marriage among the Australian aborigines. Human Biology, vol. 25, pp. 169-190.

VOGT, WILLIAM
1948. Road to survival. New York: Wm. Sloane Assoc., xvi + 335 pp., ill.

WARNER, W. L. and P. S. LUNT
1941. The social life of a modern community. New Haven: Yale Univ. Press, xviii + 460 pp.

WEIDENREICH, FRANZ
1939. The duration of life of fossil man in China and the pathological lesions found in his skeleton. Chinese Medical Journal, vol. 55, pp. 34-44. (Reprinted in *Anthropological Papers of Franz Weidenreich*, New York: The Viking Fund, 1949.)

WESTERMARCK, EDWARD
1917. The origin and development of moral ideas. (2nd ed.) London: Macmillan & Co., vol. 1, xxi + 716 pp.; vol. 2, xix + 865 pp.

WINSLOW, C. E. A.
1952. Man and epidemics. Princeton: Princeton Univ. Press, 426 pp., 17 figs.

WOYTINSKY, W. S. and E. S. WOYTINSKY
1953. World population and production trends and outlook. New York: The Twentieth Century Fund, lxxii + 1268 pp., 338 figs.

WRIGHT, QUINCY
1942. A study of war. Chicago: Univ. Chicago Press, xxiii + 1552 pp., in 2 vols.

ZINSSER, HANS
1935. Rats, lice and history; being a study in biography, which, after twelve preliminary chapters indispensable for the lay reader, deals with the life history of typhus fever. Boston: Little, Brown & Co., xii + 301 pp.

INDEX

273

N.C